# Trails to Treasure

### REVISED EDITION

- **DAVID H. RUSSELL**
- **CONSTANCE M. McCULLOUGH**
- **DORIS GATES**

**GINN AND COMPANY**

| BOSTON • NEW YORK • CHICAGO • ATLANTA |
| DALLAS • PALO ALTO • TORONTO • LONDON |

# Acknowledgments

Grateful acknowledgment is made to the following authors and publishers for permission to use and adapt copyrighted materials:

Appleton-Century-Crofts, Inc., for "The Flower-Fed Buffaloes," from *Going to the Stars*, by Vachel Lindsay. Copyright, 1926, D. Appleton & Company. Reprinted by permission of the publishers, Appleton-Century-Crofts, Inc.

Doubleday & Company, Inc., for "Gloucester Boy," adapted from *Gloucester Boy*, by Ruth and Richard Holberg; "Paul's Great Flapjack Griddle," adapted from *Paul Bunyan and His Great Blue Ox*, by Wallace Wadsworth; "A Horse Afraid of His Shadow," adapted from *Wonder Tales of Horses and Heroes*, by Frances Carpenter, copyright, 1952, by Frances Carpenter Huntington; "Rusty's Space Ship," adapted from *Rusty's Space Ship*, by Evelyn S. Lampman, copyright © 1957, by Evelyn S. Lampman; and "The Old Coach Road," reprinted from *Taxis and Toadstools*, by Rachel Field, copyright, 1926, by Doubleday & Company, Inc.; all reprinted by permission of Doubleday & Company, Inc.

E. P. Dutton & Co., Inc., for "The Bell of Atri" and "Androcles and the Lion," adapted from the book *Favorite Tales of Long Ago*, by James Baldwin, copyright, 1955, by American Book Company; and for "The Island," from the book *When We Were Very Young*, by A. A. Milne, copyright, 1924, by E. P. Dutton & Co., Inc., renewal, 1952, by A. A. Milne. All reprinted by permission of the publishers, E. P. Dutton & Co., Inc.

Alfred A. Knopf, Inc., for "Wise Alois," from *The Three Sneezes and Other Swiss Tales*, by Roger Duvoisin. Copyright, 1941, by Alfred A. Knopf, Inc., reprinted by permission of Alfred A. Knopf, Inc.; and for "The Python," from *Cautionary Verses*, by Hilaire Belloc, published, 1941, by Alfred A. Knopf, Inc., reprinted by permission of Alfred A. Knopf, Inc.

Lantern Press, Inc., for "Baseline Coach," by Charles Coombs, adapted from *Young Readers Baseball Stories*, published by Lantern Press, Inc., copyright, 1950, by Lantern Press.

The Macmillan Company, for "The Lion," from *Johnny Appleseed and Other Poems*, by Vachel Lindsay; for "Stars," from *Flame and Shadow*, by Sara Teasdale; and for "The Unexpected Fawn," from *Magical Melons*, by Carol Brink.

McGraw-Hill Book Co., Inc., for "Danny Dunn and the Anti-gravity Paint," adapted from *Danny Dunn and the Anti-gravity Paint*, by Jay Williams and Raymond Abrashkin, published by Whittlesey House, copyright © 1956, by Jay Williams and Raymond Abrashkin, by permission of McGraw-Hill Book Co., Inc.

McIntosh and Otis, Inc., for "The Feather of the Northman," from *Young Mac of Fort Vancouver*, by Mary Jane Carr. Copyright © 1940, by Mary Jane Carr. Published by Thomas Y. Crowell Co., reprinted by permission of McIntosh and Otis, Inc.

Harold Ober Associates, Inc., for "History" and "Universe" from *Poems for Children*, by Eleanor Farjeon, copyright © 1938 by Eleanor Farjeon and copyright © 1951 by Eleanor Farjeon. Both reprinted by permission of Harold Ober Associates, Incorporated.

Rinehart & Company, Inc., for "Hoosier Barbecue," by William E. Wilson, from *Picnic Adventures*, edited by Elizabeth L. Gilman, copyright, 1940, by Rinehart & Company, Inc., reprinted by permission of Rinehart & Company, Inc., New York, Publishers.

Mrs. Lew Sarett, for "The Wolf Cry," reprinted from *Many, Many Moons*,

2

by Lew Sarett. Copyrighted, 1920, by Henry Holt and Company, Inc., 1948, by Lew Sarett. Reprinted by permission of Mrs. Lew Sarett.

American Book Company, for "Androcles and the Lion," adapted from *Fifty Famous Stories Retold*, by James Baldwin.

The Bobbs-Merrill Company, Inc., for "A Girl Who Loved the Stars," adapted from *Maria Mitchell: Girl Astronomer*, by Grace Hathaway Melin, copyright © 1954, used by special permission of the publishers, The Bobbs-Merrill Company, Inc.

*Boy's Life* and Vera E. Cline, for "Two Chests of Treasure," by Merritt P. Allen, adapted by permission of the author and *Boy's Life*, published by the Boy Scouts of America.

Ann Elmo, for permission to reprint in the British Empire "Blower," adapted from *Palomino Boy*, by Don and Betty Emblen.

Follett Publishing Company, for "The Grizzly," adapted from *Redwood Pioneer*, by Betty Stirling, copyright, 1955. Published by Follett Publishing Company, Chicago, Illinois.

Mrs. Arthur Guiterman, for "Indian Pipe and Moccasin Flower," reprinted from *The Light Guitar*, by Arthur Guiterman, by permission of Mrs. Arthur Guiterman.

Harcourt, Brace and Company, Inc., for "Chica," adapted from *Chica* by Sally Scott, copyright, 1954, by Harcourt, Brace and Company, Inc.; for "Balto's Race Against Death," adapted from *Perilous Journeys*, by Irma Taylor, copyright, 1940, by Harcourt, Brace and Company, Inc.; for "The Boy and the Wolf," adapted from *The Magic Circle*, edited by Louis Untermeyer, copyright, 1952, by Harcourt, Brace and Company, Inc.; for "The Railroad Cars Are Coming," from *The American Songbag*, by Carl Sandburg, all by permission of Harcourt, Brace and Company, Inc.

Hart Publishing Company, Inc., for "Amelia Earhart," adapted from *Of Courage and Valor, Heroic Stories of Famous Men and Women*, by Jay Strong; and "The Heroes of Yellow-Jack," adapted from *A Treasury of Hero Stories*, by Joanna Strong, both by permission of the publisher, Hart Publishing Company, Inc.

Houghton Mifflin Company, for "Tara's Burro," adapted from *Golden Bird*, by Shannon Garst; and "The Long Road West," reprinted from *Songs of the Trail*, by Henry H. Knibbs; and for "Hiawatha's Hunting," reprinted from *The Song of Hiawatha*, by Henry Wadsworth Longfellow, all by permission of the publisher, Houghton Mifflin Company.

Bruce Humphries, Inc., for "Cottonwood Leaves," from *Sky Lines and Wood Smoke*, by Badger Clark, reprinted by permission of Bruce Humphries, Inc.

*The Instructor*, for "Mel's Magic Brain Machine," by William C. Gustus, copyright, 1955, by F. A. Owen Publishing Company. Adapted from *The Instructor* by permission of the publishers.

J. B. Lippincott Company and A. Watkins, Inc., for "History" and "Universe," reprinted from *Poems for Children*, by Eleanor Farjeon, copyright, 1951, by Eleanor Farjeon. Published by J. B. Lippincott Company.

Macrae Smith Company, for "With the Sunrise in His Pocket," from *Tall Tales and Tall Men*, by Nellie McCaslin, adapted by permission of the publisher, Macrae Smith Company.

Violet McDougal, for permission to reprint "The Sea Wolf."

Methuen & Co., Ltd., London, for "The Island," from *When We Were Very Young*, by A. A. Milne.

William Morrow & Company, Inc., for "The Fishing Trip," from *Henry and Ribsy*, by Beverly Cleary, copyright, 1954, by Beverly Cleary, by permission of William Morrow and Company, Inc.

*The New York Times*, for permission to reprint "The Sea Wolf," by Violet McDougal.

Maurice O'Connell, for permission to reprint "How to Tell the Wild Animals," by Carolyn Wells.

Pantheon Books, Inc., for permission to reprint "Victory," from *All Aboard*, by Mary Britton Miller.

A. D. Peters, and Gerald Duckworth & Co., Limited, London, for permission to reprint "The Python," from *Cautionary Verses*, by Hilaire Belloc.

Laurence Pollinger, Limited, London, for permission to adapt "Danny Dunn and the Anti-gravity Paint," from the book by Jay Williams and Raymond Abrashkin.

Story Parade, Inc., for "Riding the Pony Express," by Marion Garthwaite,

ILLUSTRATIONS BY Charles Andres, Harry Beckhoff, Carl Bobertz, Mel Bolden, Peter Burchard, William Caffrey, Tom Cooke, William Cummings, Roger Duvoisin, Edmund Emshwiller, Charles Freeman, George Garland, Denver Gillen, Ed Gordon, Paul Granger, Gordon Laite, Barbara Latham, Dom Lupo, Robert Magnusen, Marie Nichols, John Polgreen, Ray Quigley, Al Schmidt, Edward A. Schmitz, Fred Scott-Wood, Harve Stein, James Teason, George Wilde, and Cleveland L. Woodward

# Contents

## It Could Be You

## To Make You Laugh

## Important People

5

# Round about North America

# When Roads Led West

# Great Old Tales

# Outer Space — Fun and Fact

# In the Face of Danger

# It Could Be You

## The Fishing Trip

For several weeks Henry Huggins had been carrying a picture of himself in his mind. It showed Henry sitting in a boat pulling in a salmon —a Chinook salmon. Then he could see himself having his picture taken beside his fish and could hear people saying, "This is Henry Huggins, the boy who caught the enormous Chinook salmon."

Now Henry stood in front of the boathouse looking across the wide waters of the river's mouth. Many boats were floating out there, among them the boat in which his father and Mr. Grumbie were fishing.

10

Henry had been in that boat too. But he and his dog Ribsy had been put ashore. This had happened after Mr. Grumbie got a salmon on his line and Ribsy had jumped into the water after it. The fish had got away, and Ribsy had almost been swept out to sea before they were able to pull him back into the boat again. So Henry and his dog had been taken to shore.

The worst of it was that Scooter McCarthy was out there fishing with his father. Scooter was a little older than Henry and very proud of all the things he could do that Henry couldn't. And Henry had been foolish enough to brag about catching a Chinook salmon! There was no chance of that now. Henry could already hear the things Scooter would say to him!

"Let's go down to the beach," he said to Ribsy. "Then we won't have to see old Scooter when he comes in with all those fish he'll catch."

Henry and his dog followed a sandy road that wound through piles of driftwood, until they came to the hard wet sand along the breakers. Henry threw sticks into the breakers and watched them carried up on the sand. He picked up a few shells and pushed some jellyfish back into the water. All the time he was thinking about the salmon he wouldn't catch and wondering how he could face Mr. Grumbie on the way home. It was a terrible thing to lose a salmon after you had one on your line. If it hadn't been for Henry's dog, Mr. Grumbie would have landed his.

"Come on, Ribsy, race you!" Henry called above the roar of the ocean. Ribsy stopped chasing seagulls and ran up the beach ahead of Henry.

Henry began to have a good time. He made a game of seeing how close to the water he could run without letting the waves touch his shoes. Slowly the sun sank toward the ocean, and he knew it would not be long before his father and Mr. Grumbie would be through fishing for the day. It was time to start back to the boathouse.

"Here, Ribsy," he called.

Ribsy paid no attention. He was barking at something Henry could not see.

What's the matter with him, wondered Henry. He's excited about something. Must be a jellyfish or a crab. Maybe I'd better go look at it.

Ribsy was standing at the edge of a small stream. When Henry got there, he stopped in his tracks and stared. It wasn't true. It couldn't be. But there it was! In the shallow water at Henry's feet an enormous Chinook salmon was trying to fight its way upstream.

"Wow!" exclaimed Henry, as he watched the salmon struggle to swim in water that barely covered its silver body. The fish was so close he could see its scales and the needle-sharp teeth in its mouth. I bet he took a wrong turn. He thinks this is the river, thought Henry. Oh, why did I leave my fishing tackle in the boat?

13

"I've got to get him," Henry said to Ribsy. "I've got to, that's all."

Without stopping to take off his shoes, Henry stepped into the stream and went after the salmon. I wonder what's the best way to do this, he thought, and bent over. Carefully he put his hands into the water and then with one quick movement tried to scoop the fish up onto the sand. The salmon, which was heavier than he expected, slid easily over his hand and struggled on, fighting to get away.

Henry made up his mind that he was not going to lose that fish. He threw his rain hat and coat onto the sand. I'll tackle him, that's what I'll do, he thought.

While Ribsy frisked about and continued to bark wildly, Henry took a deep breath and threw himself onto the salmon. The icy water splashed in his face and soaked through his clothes as he gritted his teeth and hugged the big slippery fish. With one powerful lunge it twisted out of Henry's arms and tried to fight its way through water too shallow to swim in.

Dripping with water and covered with fish scales, Henry got to his feet. If I can get him onto the sand, he thought, maybe I can sit on

14

him. Once more he flung himself onto the fish and once more the salmon jerked away and landed in still shallower water.

That's it, thought Henry. I'll keep pushing him upstream.

The next time he flung himself down he managed to get one hand into the salmon's gills. They were rough and gave him something to hang onto. Henry dug in with his knees and hung on. This time the salmon didn't get away.

I've got him, but now what'll I do, thought Henry.

15

The weary salmon struggled. Henry held on. His hands ached with cold. The water was freezing. He couldn't hold on much longer.

Ribsy was running in circles, barking wildly. Henry could feel his grip on the fish's gills begin to slip. He's getting away, he thought miserably. I'll never be able to land him.

"Hang on!" someone yelled. Out of the corner of his eye Henry could see a man standing at the edge of the stream. Then the man disappeared.

Why didn't he help me, Henry wondered. But the man was soon back with a piece of wood in his hand. He waded into the stream and quickly clubbed the salmon. The fish gave one mighty flop and was still. Dripping and shivering, Henry struggled to his feet with his salmon in his arms. It was his! He had caught a Chinook!

"Well, you've caught yourself a mighty fine fish," said the man. "Must weigh twenty-five pounds at least."

Henry's teeth were chattering so he could hardly speak. "Th-th-thanks," he said as he waded out of the stream. Ribsy walked slowly toward the salmon. He sniffed at it. Then he backed away and barked.

"That's all right," answered the man. "I heard your dog barking and saw your raincoat on the sand. I thought something was wrong, so I came over." The man hung Henry's raincoat over his shoulders. "You better get dried out or you'll catch cold. Here, let me carry your salmon."

Henry didn't want to let go of his fish, but it was heavy and slippery and he was shivering so he could scarcely hang onto it.

"Yes, sir," said the man as he took the fish. "Twenty-five pounds at least."

Henry managed to grin, even though his teeth were chattering. "I'm sure glad my dog barked. I couldn't have managed if you hadn't come along to help me."

Boy, oh, boy, thought Henry, as he plodded across the sand in his wet clothes. Wait till Scooter McCarthy sees this!

17

As they neared the boathouse, Henry could hear the sound of the motors and he knew the fishermen were coming in from the river. "I think I can carry it now," he said, wanting to be sure everyone knew the fish was his. The man smiled as if he understood what Henry was thinking and handed him the salmon.

Mr. Huggins and Mr. Grumbie were just climbing the steps from the river. They looked tired, and their faces were red from the wind and the cold wet fog. To Henry's relief, Mr. Grumbie was carrying a salmon.

"Dad, look!" called Henry, trying to keep his fish from sliding out of his arms.

Mr. Huggins stared. Then he whistled.

"Caught it with his bare hands," explained the man who had helped Henry. "Yes, sir, the boy waded right into the water and tackled the fish with his bare hands. Never saw anything like it."

"And I didn't get a bite all day," said Mr. Huggins.

"Let's see how much it weighs," suggested Mr. Grumbie.

Mr. Huggins helped Henry hang his fish on the scales. Henry held his breath until the hand spun around, then stopped at twenty-nine pounds!

18

"Wow!" said Henry. His voice was almost a whisper.

All the fishermen began to talk at once. "Wait till I get my camera," said Mr. Huggins.

Henry stood proudly beside his catch while the man who had helped him told the story all over again to men who had just come from the river.

Just then Henry saw Mr. McCarthy and Scooter. Mr. McCarthy was carrying two silverside salmon and Scooter was carrying a lunch box. Henry tried to look casual as they climbed the steps.

"Hi, Scoot," he called, as Mr. Huggins returned with the camera.

"Stand close to the fish," said Mr. Huggins. He did not need to tell Henry to smile.

Henry grabbed Ribsy and made him stand at his feet. "If Ribsy hadn't barked at the salmon, I wouldn't have seen it," he explained. Ribsy kept his eye on the salmon and growled deep in his throat.

"Did you catch that fish?" asked Scooter, as the camera clicked.

"Sure," said Henry.

"With his bare hands," put in the man who had helped Henry. "Never saw anything like it. Just waded in and tackled it with his bare hands."

"How do you like that!" said Scooter. "A Chinook!"

"Come on, Henry," said Mr. Huggins, as he lifted the salmon off the scale hook. "You'd better get out of those wet clothes. There's an old coat in the trunk of the car. Get into that."

"O.K., Dad. So long, Scooter. See you around," Henry called, as he started toward the car. He felt sorry for Scooter standing there with his lunch box in his hand. It must be tough to fish all day and not catch anything.

Barking at the salmon, Ribsy trotted after Mr. Huggins.

"Good old Ribsy," said Henry.

*Beverly Cleary*

20

## The Island

If I had a ship,
I'd sail my ship,
I'd sail my ship
Through Eastern seas;
Down to a beach where the slow waves thunder—
The green curls over and the white falls under—
Boom! Boom! Boom!
On the bright sand.

Then I'd leave my ship and I'd land,
And climb the steep white sand,
And climb to the trees,
The six dark trees,
The coconut trees on the cliff's green crown—
Hands and knees
To the coconut trees,
Face to the cliff as the stones patter down,
Up, up, up, staggering, stumbling,
Round the corner where the rock is crumbling,
Round this shoulder,
Over this boulder,
Up to the top where the six trees stand.
And there would I rest, and lie,
My chin in my hands, and gaze
At the dazzle of sand below,
And the green waves curling slow,
And the gray-blue distant haze
Where the sea goes up to the sky.
And I'd say to myself as I looked so lazily down
    at the sea:
"There's nobody else in the world, and the world
    was made for me."

                                            *A. A. Milne*

# Chica

Billy sat on the front steps of the long porch. His eyes were fixed on the little road winding its way down the valley. Father was coming back that way. The question was, how was he coming?

When Woody came back in the truck alone, he hadn't said one way or another what Father was up to. "Business" was all he said. Then when Mother asked if he was getting a ride home, Woody just grinned and looked mysterious.

"He might be," he told her. "What kind, I'm not saying. And he might not be, either."

Then Mother had said, "Oh," and they both looked at Billy.

23

Billy wasn't going to ask what they meant. Woody was a terrible tease. Billy supposed all cowboys were like that. Father had been a cowboy too, but he didn't act it so much any more. Now he was too busy running the store and outfitting pack trips—busy making enough money for his family to live on.

Billy kept looking down the road. If only Father was getting him a horse of his own. He was tired of having to jog along on old plow horses. Their names would give you an idea—Nutmeg, Muley, The Ox. Just clumsy old plow horses for the pack-trip people to ride. They couldn't tell a good horse from a bad one. He wanted a real, lively, fast-stepping horse.

Woody came out of the store and sat down beside Billy. So they both saw the speck at the same time. As it came toward them and got larger, Billy could see that the black shape against the sun was a man on horseback. Billy kept looking hard. He could see Father now, and see what he was riding. It was a horse, all right. A small thin one, with floppy ears, coming along slowly.

Father brought the little mare to a stop at the steps. Billy stared at her and couldn't say a word.

24

This was lots worse than old Nutmeg! At least Nutmeg had a nice build, however old and dumb she was. But this thing looked like a bag of bones.

"Cow pony," said Father shortly. He was talking to Woody. "Well trained too, far as I can see. The man I bought her from would have kept her for himself, but she's too small to carry a man. That's why she's so thin."

Suddenly he seemed to remember Billy. "Here she is, son," he said. "Here's your horse. Like her?" He looked at Billy anxiously.

Billy had had time to think. He had thought about that Christmas years ago, when there hadn't been much money for presents. Father had worked hard making a bobsled for Billy, so he could have something nice, money or no money.

Billy had cried that Christmas morning, because what he wanted was an electric train, like one he had seen in a mail-order catalogue. Father hadn't said anything to him about it. But Mother had. Plenty! Billy still felt ashamed when he remembered what a baby he had been and how Father must have felt. He surely was old enough not to act like that now!

So when Father looked at him, Billy was all ready to pretend. "Oh, boy, Father," he said. "Is she really mine? That's swell!"

He jumped down from the porch, looking as cheerful as he could manage.

"What's her name, Father?"

"Chica," said Father.

"Could I try her out?"

Father looked pleased. "Yes, I think so. She's tired, but she's a willing horse."

Billy gathered up the reins on Chica's neck, put his foot in the stirrup, and hopped up. Chica stood quietly, waiting for orders.

Then Billy spoke to her and she moved off at once. Oh, boy, what a difference! Now he wasn't straddling Nutmeg with his legs stuck out on each side of her big barrel. His knees hugged this horse the way they should.

When they had trotted down the road a little way, Billy turned Chica and urged her into a canter. "Kabunkit, kabunkit, kabunkit!" went Chica's little hoofs. "Oh, boy!" gasped Billy.

When he pulled up at the steps, there was no pretending in his glowing face.

"Boy!" he said warmly. "She's a swell horse!"

The next morning Billy woke early. This was the day they were going to round up horses, he and Father and Woody. Billy loved to round up the horses that were always loose in the hills until they were wanted for a pack train. Today he would be riding his own horse, Chica.

Billy felt lighthearted as they started out. Father was riding Zeb, and Woody was riding Bright Boy, a new chestnut-colored horse he had traded for. Woody was training him, but the horse was still flighty.

"Means well, but no brains at all," said Woody, as the young horse jumped sideways at a bush beside the trail.

Between the two big horses, Chica cantered
merrily along, kabunkit, kabunkit, kabunkit!

"You've got a good little horse there, son,"
said Father. "She might even know something
about roundups. Why don't you and Woody go up
over the hill here and tackle the canyon together?
I'll look over the shorter draws around the flats.
If I find the horses, you come on down the canyon
and help. If you find them, chase them out to the
flats and I'll be here to turn them in the pasture
gate. O.K.?"

Billy's mouth fell open. Just he and Woody go
up the canyon? He looked anxiously at Woody,
but Woody was already swinging Bright Boy
toward the hill.

28

"Sure," Woody called out cheerfully. "Come on, Billy. I'm going to need a real good cow-hand like you to help me when this trick circus animal of mine starts rounding up horses. I've got a feeling he never heard of a roundup."

As the horses scrambled up the steep hill, Billy hoped that Chica was as well trained a cow pony as everybody said she was.

They stopped for a minute at the top to let the horses blow. They were high enough to see in both directions. Beyond them were the flats by the river, with the pasture fence beyond. Far down below them was a steep little hidden valley, half young alder trees and half open grazing.

"There they are!" said Woody, pointing.

Part way up the valley, in one of the clearings, were ten or twelve slowly moving shapes.

"I think old Nutmeg's with them," Woody said, as he took another look. "She's a mean one to catch. If she gets a chance to lead those horses back to the woods, we'll be here all day. Come on, let's go."

The horses were still in the clearing as Billy and Woody zigzagged down the hill-trail and into the valley. They raised their heads to stare at the riders, and began to bunch together.

29

"Yep, there's that Nutmeg mare," said Woody. "Hi yah!" he shouted, leaning forward in the saddle. Bright Boy burst into a gallop toward the horses, shaking with excitement and tossing his head wildly. Chica broke into a quick canter. She watched sharply as the horses milled about and then turned to stream down the valley toward the flats, with old Nutmeg out in front.

Suddenly Nutmeg turned! She was heading back for the woods! There the other horses went with her! Chica had seen it too. Before Billy could pull on the reins, she had skidded to a half stop and turned so fast she nearly had him out of the saddle.

30

Chica sped toward the woods and Billy had a glimpse of Woody pulling on the reins, as Bright Boy raced on.

Chica bored straight through on a run, ducking branches as she went. Billy hung on, his face stung by the branches and his knees bruised by the tree trunks. He hoped Chica knew what she was doing.

Suddenly they burst out of the trees onto a tiny trail. There was not a thing on it. Billy's heart sank. But the next minute from the direction of the flats came Nutmeg, leading the other horses and looking very pleased with herself.

"Hi yah!" shouted Billy, swinging Chica around to block the trail. "Go back there, Nutmeg!"

Nutmeg flung up her head, gave a loud neigh, and turned around in a hurry. The other horses turned swiftly to follow Nutmeg, and they all filed back the way they had come, with Chica racing after them.

32

When they hit the first cleared space, the horses were still rushing headlong, running too fast to think about turning off. If he got them onto the flats, Father would be there to help.

Billy shouted as loud as he could, hoping Father would hear. Where was Woody, anyway? The next minute the horses were bursting out onto the flats. They were all together still, and there came Father as fast as Zeb could gallop.

Father swung Zeb behind the horses. He looked back at Billy and waved his arm to the right. Billy turned Chica that way to block the horses if they tried to turn at the fence. Or did Chica turn herself? She streaked across the flats for the fence like a terrier chasing a rabbit.

The horses thundered up to the open gate, slid to a stop, and tried to turn. But Chica was blocking the nearest way to freedom, while Father and Zeb crowded them behind. The next minute they had pushed through the gate and galloped off into the pasture.

"Oh, boy!" shouted Billy. "We got them in."

Father looked at him proudly. "Good work, son," he said and Billy felt happy all over.

Father looked back and laughed. "Here comes Woody," he said, "looking like a porcupine."

33

There came Woody sure enough, and with all those twigs sticking out from his clothes and saddle he did look like a porcupine. Or a tree.

"This crazy horse landed me right in the middle of a dead tree," Woody said as he rode up. "Right across it!" He looked at the closed pasture gate. "See you didn't need me anyway."

"Billy brought the whole bunch in," said Father.

"Good!" said Woody. Billy swelled with pride. Then he remembered how Chica had raced through the woods, always knowing just what she was doing.

"I didn't do it really," said Billy. "It was mostly Chica. She just about rounded them up by herself."

Father looked at Billy, and if Billy had felt proud before, he felt twice as good now.

Father reached for Zeb's reins. "Billy, could you round the horses up by yourself, now they're in the pasture, and put them in the corral?"

"Sure," Billy said happily. "Chica and I can do it."

*Sally Scott*

## Baseline Coach

"Come on," Chuck Evans called. "We have a few minutes before the bell. Let's get in some practice."

"I'll go get the ball and bat," a small boy offered. His eyes were eager behind his thick glasses.

"Never mind, Clifford," Chuck said quickly. "You're too slow. One of you other fellows go get them. And hurry." Chuck, as the Bronco pitcher, was bossy at times.

"Look, Chuck," Seth said, catching up with the Bronco pitcher on the way to the diamond. "Why didn't you let Clifford go after that ball and bat? He's no ball player, but he wants to help."

"Help! He's no help," Chuck scowled. "He's always butting in. He's getting to be a pest."

"Chuck's right," Billy added. "Clifford should be seen and not heard. He's a nuisance."

Soon the crack of bat on ball could be heard on the diamond. The noises of a lively practice bounced among the giant trees that grew around the playground of District School No. 7.

It was Chuck's turn to bat. He hit a fast grounder past the pitcher's mound. The shortstop raced after it. He speared out with his glove and caught the ball. Then he straightened up and threw to second base. The second baseman touched the bag, whirled, and threw to first.

"That's the old pepper," Chuck grinned. "Just do that tomorrow when we play the Orioles and . . ."

"Way too slow," Clifford's high-pitched voice broke in from the sidelines. "Any batter would have made first easy. No real shortstop would have straightened up to throw the ball. He would have tossed underhand to second. All in one motion. Quick."

The tall red-haired pitcher walked over to Clifford, who was sitting with his back against the trunk of a tree. "Look," he said sharply, "no
36

one's asking for your help. We were playing ball before you ever heard of this school. For a new kid, you talk too much."

"I still say that the shortstop should have thrown that ball underhand," Clifford said stubbornly. "If it weren't for my glasses I'd show you what I mean."

"Oh, don't bother with him!" Billy called. "We don't need any coaching from you, Clifford."

Chuck went back to the batter's box and hit a grounder down the third baseline. Seth dipped his glove to get it. But the ball hit a small stone and went right on through his widespread legs.

"Tough luck," Chuck called. "If it hadn't been for that stone, you'd have had it. Try another—"

"In a real ball game," the shrill voice called again, "stones count. The umpire won't give you another try. Besides, that's a poor excuse. If the third baseman had held his feet close together and dropped his knee lower, the ball would never have got past him."

"Clifford," Chuck growled, "if you don't stop—"

"Besides," the newcomer went on, "where was your shortstop? He's supposed to back up third base on grounders."

Seth was the only one to smile. "Clifford, you must have swallowed a baseball rulebook."

Chuck didn't see anything to laugh about. He dropped the bat and walked over to Clifford again. Chuck was older than Clifford and large for his twelve years. He reached down, grabbed hold of Clifford's jacket and pulled him up.

"Look," he snapped, "you'd better keep quiet, or—" He pulled his arm back, as though he were going to hit the younger boy.

"Chuck Evans, what are you doing?" asked Miss Welch, their teacher, as she came around the corner of the school. "If you must pick on someone, why don't you choose a boy nearer your own size?"

The large boy's face turned red. "She saved you this time," he whispered to Clifford, "but you just try telling us what to do again and we'll fix you."

The following afternoon, the Broncos were playing the Orioles of District School No. 10. The team and a small group of rooters were taken to the other school in a bus. Clifford went along.

The Orioles were practicing when they arrived.

"This is going to be a tough game," said one of the Broncos. "Look how big they are."

"Play ball!" the captain of the Orioles called.

The Broncos were up first, and Billy led off. The Oriole pitcher threw a curved ball that was hard to hit. Billy soon found that out. Two more Broncos found it out right after him.

The Orioles came to bat. The first man sent a fly to second base. The second batter hit a short fly along the left field baseline. The Bronco left fielder came racing in to catch it, but the ball went right between his legs and kept on rolling. It was a home run for the Oriole batter.

"Keep those feet together!" Clifford yelled.

A high foul, caught by the catcher, then a grounder to first, ended the inning.

Score, Orioles 1; Broncos 0.

The first Bronco batter started the second inning by waving at two pitches that curved inside.

"Step back on those," Clifford yelled. "Step back and hit that ball."

"If you don't keep quiet—" Chuck glared over his shoulder, but the crack of the bat on the ball made him jerk his head around. A line drive was just clearing the second baseman's outstretched glove. The ball sailed on into right field for a double, then Seth's single brought the batter in.

Later, Chuck said, "What's the secret? I thought that pitcher had your number."

Breathless from his run, the batter glanced over at Clifford. "I don't know," he whispered. "I stepped back from the plate, just the way he said, and hit the ball right on the nose."

"Luck, I guess," Chuck said carelessly.

The Orioles scored two runs in the second inning. The third and fourth innings were scoreless. In the Broncos' half of the fifth, Chuck came to bat with a runner on first.

"Bunt him to second," Clifford yelled.

But Chuck didn't bunt. He swung hard at the ball, and hit a grounder that headed straight for third. The third baseman made a neat double play and two Broncos went out.

40

"Maybe Clifford was right," Seth told Chuck. "Maybe a bunt would have been the smart thing."

"When I let Clifford tell me what to do," Chuck snapped, "I'll eat your hat!"

"I'll remember that," Seth smiled. "And here's hoping we get another chance like that one."

The chance came in the first of the seventh inning. There were runners on first and third when Billy came up to bat.

"Hit it, Billy," Clifford shouted. "Hit it out of the lot."

Billy did hit it, but he was tagged out for trying to reach third base. Two runs came in, however, tying the score. The next batter struck out. The score was 3 to 3 at the end of the seventh inning and no one scored in the eighth.

In the first of the ninth the Bronco shortstop led off with a single into short center field. Chuck wouldn't admit that the unwelcomed sideline coaching had anything to do with it, but he told the next batter to bunt. It worked. When the Orioles came up to bat, the Broncos were leading by one very important run.

At the last of the ninth the Broncos were in a bad spot. The Orioles had runners on first and third. Chuck lost control for a minute and walked a batter to load the bases.

Then he wound up and pitched again. The Oriole batter hit a high bouncing grounder toward shortstop. The shortstop scooped up the ball. He

42

had to make a double play. He straightened up, whirled and threw to second base, and second baseman sent the throw to first.

But a split second had slipped by. That split second was the difference between one and two out. The game was over. Orioles 5; Broncos 4.

"Any big-league shortstop would have used an underhand throw . . . all one smooth motion," Clifford said sadly, as they walked to the bus.

"A lot you know about what a big-league shortstop would do," Chuck said grouchily.

Early next morning Billy came flying into the Evans yard. "The Giants are in Center City," he shouted. "They're going to play a practice game with the Center City team. Dad said he'd take our whole team to see them. Can you go?"

Chuck ran to ask his mother, and came back shouting, "It's O.K.!"

"Good," said Billy. "I'll call the others."

A few hours later, the boys sat in the grandstand of the Center City Ball Park. Everyone was talking at once.

"There's Jojo Smith at shortstop," Andy said. "He's tops in the big league."

"Hey," Chuck shouted. "Look down there by the dugout, isn't—isn't that—"

43

"It sure is," Billy cried. "It's Clifford!"

The Giants soon came in from their fielding practice, and the game started.

Suddenly Clifford's voice sounded from the Giants' dugout. He was yelling, "No outs, Jojo. Play it safe!"

"Of all the nerve," said Chuck. "Telling Jojo Smith how to play. They should throw him out."

But Jojo just smiled. "Safe it is, Cliffie!"

It was a good practice game and the big-league team won. But the Broncos were too surprised to cheer.

"Here comes Clifford," Seth pointed.

"Pretend you don't see the show-off!" said Chuck.

Clifford came up to them. "I'd like you to come to the locker room to meet my brother and the rest of the Giants," he said.

"Your what?" asked Chuck.

"My brother, Jojo Smith, the shortstop."

For a moment no one spoke. Then the Broncos began to talk all at once.

"What's so special about that?" asked Clifford. "Lots of players have kid brothers. I'm Jojo's."

The Broncos had nothing to say as they followed Clifford down the ramp to the locker room.

"As soon as Cliffie's eyes get used to his new glasses, he'll be able to play with you," Jojo said. "He knows a lot about baseball. He spent two weeks with me last year during spring training. I think he'll be a Giant someday."

Outside the locker room, Chuck said eagerly, "Cliffie, how would you like to coach the Broncos? Be a real coach, the kind all the fellows have to listen to?"

"Here's your dinner," said Seth as he took off his baseball cap and handed it to Chuck.

For a moment Chuck was puzzled, then he remembered. "Hey," he said, "does anybody have a bottle of catsup?"

*Charles Coombs*

45

# Godfrey Gordon Gustavus Gore

Godfrey Gordon Gustavus Gore—
No doubt you have heard the name before—
Was a boy who never would shut a door!

The wind might whistle, the wind might roar,
And teeth be aching and throats be sore,
But still he never would shut the door.

His father would beg, his mother implore,
"Godfrey Gordon Gustavus Gore,
We really *do* wish you would shut the door!"

Their hands they wrung, their hair they tore;
But Godfrey Gordon Gustavus Gore
Was deaf as the buoy out at the Nore.

When he walked forth the folks would roar,
"Godfrey Gordon Gustavus Gore,
Why don't you think to shut the door?"

They rigged out a Shutter with sail and oar,
And threatened to pack off Gustavus Gore
On a voyage of penance to Singapore.

But he begged for mercy, and said, "No more!
Pray do not send me to Singapore
On a Shutter, and then I will shut the door!"

"You will?" said his parents; "then keep on shore!
But mind you do! For the plague is sore
Of a fellow that never will shut the door,
Godfrey Gordon Gustavus Gore!"

*William Brighty Rands*

47

## Two Stripes against Him

Barbara saw it first. She stopped to look more closely at something black and white that was under the hedge.

"What are you looking at?" her brother asked her and slowed his steps.

"It's a cat—I think," Barbara answered slowly. "No. It's a skunk!"

Dave's eyes followed her pointing finger and then widened with fear. He backed a few steps, pulling Barbara with him.

"A skunk!" He started pulling her down the hill. "Let's get out of here!"

48

Barbara shook off his hand. "It's a beautiful animal," she said. "I want to see more of it."

She began walking slowly back toward the hedge.

"Come on, silly," Dave called to her. "Don't you know anything about skunks?"

"Of course I know about skunks," said Barbara. "I know they have scent glands near their tails. When they are frightened, they shoot a bad-smelling spray at you. It stings, too, if it gets into your eyes. Other animals know this and so they let skunks alone."

"And you'd better let this one alone," Dave said darkly, but he didn't really think she would.

Barbara turned to smile over her shoulder at Dave. She looked as if a wonderful idea had come into her head.

"You know, Dave," she said happily, "I think this may be a tame skunk. If he is, his scent glands must have been removed. He doesn't seem to be a bit afraid of me." She turned back to the skunk and put out her hand slowly. "Here, skunk. Here, skunk," she called softly.

49

She was quite close to the hedge now. The little black-and-white animal had stuck his striped head out from under the hedge and was looking at the two children with eyes as bright as two jet buttons.

"When he turns around, you'd better be ready to run," Dave warned her.

Barbara crouched down. "Come here, skunk," she said. "We won't hurt you."

Barbara was one of those lucky people who know just how to talk to animals. There was something in her voice now which made the skunk understand that she loved all animals on sight, even skunks. Slowly he came from under the hedge.

"He's beautiful," breathed Barbara.

He was beautiful. His black-and-white tail arched over his back. Two stripes of white ran up his body. He was not quite so large as a cat, but his fur was longer.

He walked slowly toward Barbara's waiting hand. At last his little pointed nose bumped it. Next he put two paws on her hand and looked up into her face.

Dave watched as Barbara's other hand went gently around the striped body. Then she lifted the skunk into her arms, getting slowly and quietly to her feet.

50

"I hope you're not making a mistake," said Dave, still keeping a good distance away. "What are you going to do with him?"

"Take him home, of course," Barbara said. "I think this is a lost tame skunk. We'll watch the newspaper and see if anybody has lost a skunk. If not, he'll be our pet."

They started down the hill with the skunk riding on Barbara's shoulder, his tail waving like a plume.

"Maybe after dinner Daddy will take him over to the vet's to find out about his scent glands," Barbara said.

"Not tonight he won't," Dave told her. "This is the night we're supposed to go to Mr. Parker's to see the pictures he brought back from his trip around the world."

The Turner children usually stopped in the kitchen to get a doughnut or a handful of ginger cookies when they came home from school. This time, however, Barbara walked right past the cookie jar and headed straight for the living room.

"Hello, Mother," she called. "See what I have."

Mrs. Turner had raised her eyes from her work to smile at her children as they came into the room. Suddenly her smiling welcome changed to fear as she caught sight of the black- and-white animal.

"Barbara, get that animal out of here! At once!" Her voice was just below a scream.

"I warned you," said Dave, edging past his sister and into the living room.

"He's tame, Mother," Barbara said. "I'm going to call him Stripes."

"Get out!" cried her mother again. This time it was a scream.

Barbara had never heard her mother scream before. She turned quickly and went back to the kitchen. A door led straight from the kitchen into the garage. Barbara went through that door.

She hunted around in the garage until she found a large cardboard carton. Then she carefully put Stripes into it. Next she pushed the carton over to the pile of fireplace wood and laid a piece of wood on the cover.

After she had made some small holes in the carton and was sure that Stripes was safe and comfortable, she returned to the living room.

This was the way it always happened when Barbara showed up at home with a strange pet. Mrs. Turner would tell her to get it out at once, Barbara would take it to the garage, and after some arguing, Mrs. Turner would give in.

This time things were different.

53

"Barbara, I won't have a skunk on the place," her mother told her as soon as Barbara walked into the room. She held up her hand as her daughter started to argue. "I have been most understanding about your love for animals. I have risked finding snakes in my bed, mice in my kitchen, a woodchuck in the yard, even a white rat in the cellar, but I won't risk having a skunk anywhere around this house."

"Oh, Mother," begged Barbara, "Stripes isn't a risk. He's tame. Really he is. Now tell me, do you smell him at all?"

"No, I don't smell him yet," said Mrs. Turner, "and with luck I won't. We'll leave him right where you've put him for the night because I'm sure you haven't turned him loose. I don't want to start any trouble with him before we go to Mr. Parker's. But tomorrow morning he must go."

When Mr. Turner came home, he was also sure that the skunk must go. He did say, however, that he had heard somewhere, maybe on the radio or television, that skunks could be model pets.

After supper Barbara gave Stripes something to eat. She put a dish of water in his carton. The skunk let her pat his head and seemed quiet. Then she left with the family for the Parkers'.
54

While Mr. Parker was getting ready to show his pictures, they all talked about the thief who had been breaking into houses in their town.

"It's too bad," said Mrs. Parker. "We've felt so safe in our little out-of-the-way town. I hope they catch him soon."

"They will," said her husband, "don't you fear." He was ready to show the pictures now. "Dave, will you turn off that electric light next to you? Here we go!"

The pictures were in color. Quite a few were of animals—elephants, giraffes, camels, and many more. Barbara liked them all. Dave found the pictures of Tensing and Mt. Everest the most interesting. Tensing was one of the two men who were the first to climb Mt. Everest. Dave wanted to climb to high mountain peaks like Tensing.

After the pictures, they had lemonade and ice cream and cake. Then the Turners said good night and started home. They were almost there, and Dave was still talking about Mt. Everest and Tensing when he was stopped short by his mother. "There's a light in our dining room!" she exclaimed. "I'm sure I turned off all the lights."

"Funny," Barbara said. "It's not a very bright light. I wonder what it can be."

"Looks as if it were on the floor," said Dave.

"Sam!" exclaimed Mrs. Turner. "That's just about as much light as a flashlight would give. Do you suppose . . . ?"

Mr. Turner slowed the car, but his voice was quiet as he said, "Now, Mary, don't get excited."

56

He stopped the car in the driveway. Dave started to get out to open the garage door, but his father stopped him.

"I want you to stay here in the car and lock all the doors," he said, getting out of the car himself.

They watched as he went quietly around to the dining-room window. Suddenly he returned to the car, walking fast, and motioning for them to be as quiet as possible.

"Get out, all of you, and come with me to the Harpers'," he said in a hushed voice.

They all got out and followed him to the house next door.

"What happened?" asked Mrs. Turner.

"Can't say for sure," he said, "but I think I had better call the police."

They waited at the Harpers' until the police car drove up. Then Mr. Turner went with the policemen to his own house. In just a few minutes he was back, laughing.

"You may all come home now," he told his family.

The Harpers went along with the Turners to see what had happened. Two policemen were standing in the dining room.

Stretched out on the floor of the dining room was a heavy cloth. On the cloth was Mrs. Turner's silver, and walking slowly around the dining-room table was Stripes. Barbara ran to him and lifted him into her arms.

"How did you get out?" she asked.

"It's all very clear," said one of the policemen. "The thief got into the house through the door from the garage to the kitchen. The skunk must have got out of his box and followed him. The thief just had time to lay the silver out when he caught the skunk in the beam from his flashlight.

"That did it. He ran out the front door so fast he forgot to pick up anything. He didn't want to argue with a skunk. The silver wouldn't have been that big a prize!"

"Now how about letting me keep Stripes?" asked Barbara eagerly.

Mrs. Turner put an arm around her daughter and the skunk. "If he's as good a pet as he is a watchdog, I don't see how we can get along without him," she said.

Next day Mr. Turner and his children took Stripes to the vet. Just as Barbara had guessed, the skunk's scent glands had been removed.

For several days after that, they watched the papers, but no one seemed to want Stripes back. So Barbara kept her pet. As for the thief, Stripes must have frightened him out of town. He was never heard from again!

*Doris Gates*

# Oliver and the Model T

Adele Treadway finished her soda with a sigh, drank water through what was left of her straw, and began whispering her promised news. Oliver Ott and her brother, Lincoln, better known as the Missing Link, listened eagerly.

"They're planning the town's birthday party," Adele said. "The committee met in Daddy's office this afternoon. I was there and I heard everything. They have a wonderful idea. They are going to hold an endurance race for automobiles and give a prize to the oldest car that can drive around town without breaking down."

The Link snorted scornfully, "What a silly idea! Who cares about a lot of old cars? Why couldn't they have a real race with modern sports cars?"

"Why, Lincoln Treadway," cried Adele. "Those old cars made this town. It was nothing but a mudhole until people bought cars and built a highway. Why our road was the first real highway in the state. It's part of our history and so are those old cars."

"Well! you can count me out," said the Link. "I'm not going to bother to see this endurance race. And what's more, your news isn't worth a nickel."

"Don't be so sure," said Oliver, the boy genius of Harmony Village. "You're going to be my partner in this race."

"We—in the endurance race?" The Link's voice cracked. "But we haven't even got a car."

"It's against the law for kids to drive," said Adele.

"I know that! But I've got a plan and you know that Ott, the boy genius, never fails."

Adele's eyes became bigger, but Oliver didn't give her a chance to say anything. "We must act fast," he went on. "We're going to—never mind where. To your bicycles!"

The children started along a stretch of road that had been part of the nation's first coast-to-coast highway. Now it was rough and badly in need of repair. The new highway by-passed Harmony and few tourists ever bothered to visit the town.

Joe White's garage stood at the top of a hill on the old road. Once it had been crowded with cars and trucks. Now it was a ghost garage on a ghost road.

The three children stopped their bikes and looked around for Joe. There was no sign of him, except his legs sticking out from under a car. They called, and he came crawling out.

"What is it, Oliver? Your bicycle?" he asked.

"Not my bicycle," Oliver answered. "It's about automobiles, and it's a chance for you to make some money and show this town what an A-1 mechanic you are." Oliver went on to paint the coming celebration in glowing colors—the bunting, the flags, and the cheering crowds. The Firemen's Band would lead a big parade. Then, the biggest event of all, the old cars polished up—

Joe stopped him. "Sounds very nice, but what has it got to do with me?"

"Why, Joe, you're going to enter the old Model T that's standing in your barn."

62

"Dad's old car? It hasn't been out of the shed for years. She's old, Oliver. Why, she was made in 1910. Even if I could get her started, I don't think I could get her to go all around town."

"Well, think it over, Joe," urged Oliver. "If you change your mind, we three can help a lot. We'll be back in the morning."

Next morning, right after breakfast, the three appeared at Joe's garage. They wore old play clothes and carried their lunches in paper bags.

A surprise awaited them. Joe's old Model T had been pushed to the center of the garage. Short and square with gleaming brass headlights, she stood high on her wheels. She was a leftover from the days of dirt roads when twenty miles an hour was as fast as most cars traveled.

63

Joe looked at the children with a grin. "I've changed my mind," he said. "Old T is a grand old car. The only real problem is the tires. If we can get two tires for her, we can charge the battery, and fix her up so she'll win that race."

From then on they all worked steadily. Oliver cleaned and oiled each part of the car until it looked like new. The Link proved to be useful with a paint gun. Adele polished all the brass.

But none of them had been able to find two tires. Then Grandpa Treadway remembered Dr. Castle. Doc had used a Model T for years. Grandpa was sure he hadn't sold it. That's how Adele happened to come plodding into the garage with two tires hung around her shoulders. The boys cheered her. The Link even gave his sister a hug.

Three days before the birthday party, Old T was to make a test run.

Her engine was ready to be started by the hand crank that hung under the radiator. "Oliver, you sit in the driver's seat," said Joe, as he seized the crank. "When I crank her, you fix the spark and keep her going."

Joe cranked and Old T started coughing in a lady-like way. Joe cranked some more. Old T coughed some more. Then, without any warning,

64

the old car came to life with a roar. It began acting like a mad beast. It headed straight for Link. The Link jumped one way, Adele another.

Oliver's hands were frozen to the wheel. Just ahead was the garage door. With some idea that fresh air might help, Oliver headed Old T into the open. There was a loud crash as the car rammed into the gas pump and stopped.

Old T stood with front wheels against the pump, dripping oil and gas. Steam was shooting out of her battered radiator, one fender and one running board were wrecked, and one tire was flat.

Oliver crawled out and looked at it. "I must have made a slight mistake," he said. Suddenly his knees were shaky. He sat down and closed his eyes. When he opened them, Joe was beside him, offering him a drink of water.

"How do you feel?" asked Joe.

"Terrible," moaned Oliver. "I've wrecked our old Model T."

"Don't worry about the outside, and maybe I can fix the inside. Those old Fords were mighty tough."

Joe found plenty the matter with the engine, but the worst thing was a leak in the carburetor.

"Maybe the carburetor on Dr. Castle's old Ford is still good," said Adele. It was, and two days later Old T was ready to be cranked again. This time the hand brake was set and her wheels were blocked.

The old car was full of rattles, but Joe was sure none of them were important. The battered radiator was somewhat straightened, and the flat tire had been patched. The new fender, bought in a junk yard, was too large, but it would keep mud from splashing over them.

The day of the celebration was gray and cloudy. The roads were still wet from a storm the night

66

before. But Harmony's citizens decorated their stores and their houses with flags and bunting, and got ready for the parade.

The starting point for the afternoon's race was to be the race track at the fairgrounds. Crowds arrived early to look at the cars which were being exhibited in a big shed near the track.

The oldest automobile was a 1905 electric. Its owner wasn't sure he could finish the race. The batteries in the old electrics went dead after about thirty miles, but he was going to try.

There was a 1907 Stanley Steamer having its boiler filled with water. The owner of a bright-red 1913 Stutz racer was telling about how much speed he could get out of it.

All the old cars in the line-up looked in A-1 condition. They had new coats of paint and beautifully polished brass. Poor Old T didn't look nearly as smart, but across her back was a big sign: EXCUSE MY DUST!

The time for the big event was drawing near, and a signal was given to clear the shed. The children joined Joe and Old T just as the last group of people was leaving. They were dressed just right for a ride in a 1910 Ford. Adele even wore a veil.

"Where did you get those clothes?" asked Joe.

"When my mother saw the parade she remembered that she had some old-fashioned clothes that belonged to my grandma and grandpa," said Oliver. "And here they are!"

"Well, don't trip over them. Climb in," said Joe. "The race will start any minute."

The mayor stated the rules of the race and called out the cars, one by one. They were to drive around the track in turn so people could see them in action. Then they would start on the course around the town.

"Number Eighteen!" called the mayor. "Ford, Model T, 1910, owned by Joe White. Exhibited by Joe White, Oliver Ott, Adele Treadway, and Lincoln Treadway!"

68

Oliver cranked her up while his heart skipped a beat. At last the engine gave a cough and started. Oliver climbed in beside Joe. Adele and the Link sat in the back.

Old T made the first part of the route without any trouble. But so did all the other cars. The part that caused the trouble was the rough dirt stretch on the old Reed's Hill Road. It had deep ruts and was slippery with oil and mud.

The electric car was at the side of the road. Part way up was the Stanley Steamer—stalled. One car after another was skidding off the road.

Joe stopped a second at the foot of the hill to shift gears. The Stutz racer splashed by. It's driver shouted, "Are you giving up?"

"We are not!" yelled Oliver. Then he looked at Joe and asked, "Or are we?"

"Of course not," said Joe. "Our car is the oldest one left and if we make it, the prize is ours."

Old T began to climb. They crawled and slipped. Everyone was shouting at Joe, telling him what to do. The old car was slipping faster and faster as it splashed through a puddle. Joe straightened it out and they went forward a few feet. Then they lost a few feet. Then Old T was on its way again.

They saw the Stutz racer stuck in the mud. "That won't happen to us," said Joe. But something else was happening. Their car was sliding now, skidding slowly. The people along the road became silent. Joe gritted his teeth. Then he swung the old car around until they had turned back to front. Her nose was pointing down hill. People laughed at them, but they soon stopped. Old T was climbing Reed's Hill backwards!

One painful stop made them hold their breath but Joe gave her more gas and away they went over the last hump to the old brick road above. Joe turned Old T so that her nose faced forward and they chugged ahead.

70

"That was hard work," said Joe. "I thought we were done for until I remembered that the power is in the rear wheels. They grip the road better than the front ones. Whenever my father was stuck on Reed's, that's how he got to the top."

The Firemen's Band played "Hail to the Chief," as they drove into the fairgrounds.

Joe steered the car around the track and honked the horn. Oliver tipped his hat, Adele and the Link bowed, and they all grinned. They had won the Old Automobile Endurance Race.

*Jack Bechdolt*

# Things to Think About and Do

1. Be a good detective and skim each story in this unit for clues that tell when the story took place. List the clues under these headings.

Season of the Year
Time of Day at the Beginning of the Story
Time of Day at the End of the Story

2. Tell how each of the following is a sign of "growing up." Find other signs in the stories.

The Link even gave his sister a hug.
"I didn't do it really. It was mostly my horse."
It must be tough to fish all day and not catch anything.
"Be a real coach, the kind all the fellows have to listen to."
He felt hot all over when he remembered how Father must have felt.

3. Make a list of words that describe each of the following characters. Then write a short paragraph about each one using the words from your list.

Henry Huggins          Chuck Evans
Joe White              Dave Turner
Woody                  Adele Treadway

4. Suppose the newspaper printed the picture which Mr. Huggins took of Henry and his Chinook salmon. Write a headline and a short newspaper story about the picture.

72

5. "Chica" would make a good "Western" for a television program. List the scenes for such a program. You might start with the one below.

Scene I. Billy Waits for His Father

6. Godfrey Gordon Gustavus Gore had a bad habit. Write five sentences about five bothersome habits you are trying to break.

7. Ask a friend to help you plan a make-believe conversation between Barbara and her mother. One of you may be Barbara and give good reasons why you should keep the skunk. The other may be Mother and give good reasons why you will not let Barbara keep a skunk. Ask your class to listen and decide which of you gave the best reasons.

8. Find route U.S. 30 on a road map of the United States. This was the first coast-to-coast highway. Where does it begin? Where does it end? All the stories in this unit could have taken place in one of the states through which route 30 travels. What state would you guess for each story? Be prepared to give a good reason for each guess.

9. Make posters announcing Harmony's Old Automobile Endurance Race. Tell What? Where? When? and Why?

# Some Books to Read

*Cabin Boy and Extra Ballast*, by Barbara Leonard Reynolds.

An American family in Japan sail their boat to Honolulu. Danger and excitement sail with them.

*Henry and the Paper Route*, by Beverly Cleary.

More funny adventures of Henry Huggins as he decides to go into business.

*Ride Like an Indian*, by Henry V. Larom.

Jerry's summer on a dude ranch becomes a happy vacation after he forms a warm friendship with an Indian boy who teaches him to ride.

*Sally Saucer*, by Edna S. Weiss.

Sally had no playmates so she welcomed Penny who came to stay with grandmother Saucer on the farm.

*That Jud!* by Elspeth Bragdon.

After his father's death at sea, Jud feels lonely and unwanted even though the Maine villagers try to help him.

*This Boy Cody and His Friends*, by Leon Wilson.

Cody lives in Cumberland Gap and has wonderful times, most of them in the great outdoors. Some of his best friends are animals.

*Bigity Anne*, by Helen Fern Daringer.

A family of four children measure up to responsibility.

# To Make You Laugh

## Mel's Magic Brain Machine

Miss Curtis was about to start class when she noticed the fairly large brown wooden box on the floor beside the new boy. It looked a little too mysterious to be a homemade lunch box.

"Melvin, we do not keep our belongings in the classroom," she said. "Would you put your box with your wraps, please?"

Mel tucked the box under his arm and started toward the cloakroom. He could almost feel the curious eyes following him—and the box. He knew he would be stopped before he could get very far. And he was!

76

"Melvin, since everyone seems so curious about your box, suppose you tell us what's in it." It was not hard to tell that Miss Curtis was as curious as everyone else. That was the way Mel had planned it.

Mel's father was an officer in the Navy, and it seemed as if his family was on the move three or four times a year. No sooner was Mel settled in a new school than he had to leave. No sooner did he make new friends than he had to say good-by to them. The first half-dozen times he had been very lonely, but that was all over now. On his first day in a new school he just tucked his mysterious box under his arm, and that settled it.

He tightened his fingers around the box and turned to face Miss Curtis.

"It's nothing, Miss Curtis," he said. "Just a little invention of mine."

"Oh, so you're an inventor." Still curious, she asked, "What have you invented?"

"Just a brain machine," Mel said. "It makes people twice as smart as they are."

Miss Curtis smiled. You could tell she didn't believe a word of it. Everyone else in the room grinned. Some of them even laughed out loud. A brain machine!

"You may explain later how your machine works," Miss Curtis said, "but put it away until then, please."

Mel went to the cloakroom sure that he would not have to spend his first recess in this school standing alone in the corner of the yard.

How right he was! At recess the fun began. In no time the whole class had crowded around him, eager to be friends with an inventor, eager to try out his brain machine. Usually Mel would have let anybody try the machine and have had a lot of fun, but today something went wrong. A rather big boy pushed his way through the crowd until he stood almost chin to chin with Mel.

78

"My name is Paul Briggs, and I say that your invention is a fake—and so are you!"

Mel tried to laugh, but he saw that Paul Briggs was very serious about what he said. Mel wanted to explain that the whole thing was a joke—a trick to make friends. But there was something about the way Paul spoke that kept him from it.

"Well, is it a fake, or isn't it?"

Mel looked at the anxious expressions of the children around him. Somehow it would be like backing down if he agreed with Paul Briggs, and yet, he couldn't say that the brain machine wasn't a fake.

Paul Briggs reached into the crowd and seized a boy by the arm. "Come out here, Davey," he said, pulling a much smaller boy into the middle of the circle. "Davey is the dumbest one in the spelling class. That right, Davey?"

Davey nodded his head.

"The most he ever got right was four words out of ten—and he must have been lucky that day. If this machine isn't a fake, prove it by making Davey a good speller."

79

Mel wondered what to do next. The whole thing was silly. Of course he couldn't make Davey a good speller. He wanted to explain, but it was becoming harder and harder. He could tell from the expressions on the faces of the children that they were counting on him to put Paul Briggs in his place.

Mel never did know if it was because he didn't want to disappoint them, or because he was just plain foolish, but he heard himself saying, "You've asked for a demonstration, and a demonstration you shall have." As if that wasn't enough, he added, "Mel's magic brain machine has never been known to fail."

"That's what you say!" Paul Briggs laughed. "Let's see you give Davey a treatment then."

"Right you are," Mel said, trying to act very sure of himself. As he opened the box, however, the bell rang to end recess.

"I'll be right here after school," Paul Briggs said.

All through the rest of the school day Mel kept trying to decide what he should do. He didn't want a boy like Paul Briggs to get the better of him. His plan was crazy, but he was going to carry it off to the finish.

80

After school there were three times as many children gathered in the yard as there had been at recess. They all crowded around Mel to watch Davey get a treatment.

Mel had Davey sit on the school steps. Then he slowly opened the cover of his mysterious brown box and took out a navy blue cap. The cap had a propeller on the top mounted on a thin metal tube. There was a long rubber hose leading from the metal tube to a hand pump inside the brown box. He placed the cap on Davey's head, and the treatment was ready to begin.

Mel pumped away, and the propeller began to whirl faster and faster. A strange look came over Davey's face. This was caused by the air whipping against his head, but no one knew that.

As he worked, Mel kept repeating a little rhyme which he had made up during lunch:

"Around and around she goes,
And where she stops, nobody knows.
After this, there's just no telling
How good Davey will be in spelling."

When the treatment ended, there were only a few laughs. Maybe everyone was hoping that Mel was a real magician whose machine did work magic.

Mel put his invention away carefully. "Today is Monday," he said. "The next spelling test is Friday. In just four days you'll see that Mel's magic brain machine really works."

As the crowd broke up, Mel overheard two girls talking. "If it would only work," said one, "maybe it would teach that awful Paul Briggs something."

The other answered, "I wish it would, too, but if Miss Curtis can't teach Davey how to spell, I'm afraid no magic brain machine can either."

At last only Mel and Davey were left together.

"You don't know what you let yourself in for," Davey said. "Paul was right. I'm dumb in spelling, but anyway thanks for trying to help me."

"I promise you'll do better this Friday, Davey," Mel said. "I'm counting on you."

82

"Somehow you make me feel that maybe I will," Davey said.

The next three days the new words seemed so hard that you would have thought Miss Curtis was working against Mel and Davey, even though she didn't know a thing about the treatment. With each new word Paul Briggs's eyes gleamed.

On Friday, the morning of the test, Miss Curtis wondered why the class was so restless. She may even have wondered where the sudden interest in spelling had come from, for this morning everyone sat with pens ready, waiting eagerly for the first word.

Then the important test began. Miss Curtis pronounced each word, used it in a sentence, and pronounced it again. After each word everyone stared at Davey. Davey sat grimly clutching his pen. His eyes never left his paper.

Finally Miss Curtis said, "The last word is *ab bre vi a tion.*" She used it in a sentence and repeated it, then she read all ten words again.

As the papers were being handed in, the excitement grew too great. A boy in the back row just had to raise his hand and explain the whole thing to Miss Curtis. When she had heard the whole story, she smiled a little.

83

Paul Briggs raised his hand and grinned at Mel as he asked, "Miss Curtis, you don't believe in brain machines either, do you?"

"Well, Paul," Miss Curtis answered, "I don't quite know if I believe in brain machines or not. Let's find out." She dug Davey's paper out of the pile and ran her blue pencil slowly down the words.

Everyone was breathlessly quiet now, and Mel wished he could crawl into his brown box and pull down the cover. He listened as Miss Curtis counted. Already she had reached five. Was it five right or five wrong?

Softly she finished her count, ". . . six . . . seven . . . eight." Then she placed a mark at the

top of the paper. A puzzled expression showed on her face as she held up the paper. "Eight right," she said. "I don't know how you did it, Davey, but keep up the good work."

Mel's surprise was greater than the relief he felt. He could hardly wait for recess to come so he could talk to Davey. When they were together, he said, "See, Davey? Mel's magic brain machine has never been known to fail." Almost in the same breath he asked, "How did you do it?"

"I guess I just worked harder," Davey said. "It was wonderful having a chance to show up Paul Briggs, the way he was trying to show you up."

"Well, it proves what you can do if you think you can. But listen, Davey, we won't let on to the others that the brain machine is a fake, will we? Let's keep them guessing."

"But it isn't a fake!" Davey shouted. "It made me work harder. It made me think I could do better, and it made me get eight words out of ten right. That's twice as many as I ever got right before. Why I even spelled *abbreviation* right!"

Mel sat down to think that one over. For all he knew, he might be another Thomas Edison!

*William C. Gustus*

# How to Tell the Wild Animals

If ever you should go by chance
    To jungles in the East;
And if there should to you advance
    A large and tawny beast,
If he roars at you as you're dyin'
You'll know it is the Asian Lion.

Or if some time when roaming round,
    A noble wild beast greets you,
With black stripes on a yellow ground,
    Just notice if he eats you.
This simple rule may help you learn
The Bengal Tiger to discern.

If strolling forth, a beast you view,
    Whose hide with spots is peppered,
As soon as he has lept on you,
    You'll know it is the Leopard.
'Twill do no good to roar with pain,
He'll only lep and lep again.

86

If when you're walking round your yard,
    You meet a creature there,
Who hugs you very, very hard,
    Be sure it is the Bear.
If you have any doubt, I guess
He'll give you just one more caress.

Though to distinguish beasts of prey
    A novice might nonplus,
The Crocodiles you always may
    Tell from Hyenas thus:
Hyenas come with merry smiles;
But if they weep, they're Crocodiles.

The true Chameleon is small,
    A lizard sort of thing;
He hasn't any ears at all,
    And not a single wing.
If there is nothing on the tree,
    'Tis the Chameleon you see.

*Carolyn Wells*

87

# "With the Sunrise in His Pocket"

*A Radio Play*

*Based on tall tales about Davy Crockett*

## THE CHARACTERS

FIRST STORYTELLER
SECOND STORYTELLER
DAVY CROCKETT
RATTLER, *his dog*
DEATH HUG, *his bear*
MISSISSIPPI, *his alligator*

FIRST STORYTELLER. We in America have a great many heroes that we do not know much about. One of these is Davy Crockett. He was a hunter, an Indian fighter, a scout in the wilderness, and a member of Congress.

88

As a member of Congress, Davy Crockett was a spokesman for the settlers who were moving westward and building their cabins in the American wilderness.

Davy Crockett liked to talk about his adventures, and many a story has come down to us through the years. Some of them are, of course, true. Others are the tall tales which grow up around a hero as colorful as Davy Crockett. We are going to tell you some of these tall tales now, just as we heard them.

SECOND STORYTELLER. In a way Davy Crockett was a giant. At least he started out that way. Like all giants he was an unusual baby. He himself told how he was rocked to sleep in the shell of a great snapping turtle. He had a tawny panther's skin for a cover, and a crocodile curled itself right up in a ball to make him a pillow. Yes, sir, he slept with his head on a live crocodile.

FIRST STORYTELLER. One of the things everybody seemed to remember most about him was his grin. Why, it was famous all over the country.

When he was a boy, he used to grin the way other people would shoot a gun—he'd get what he wanted just by grinning at it! Once when he needed a cap, he saw a raccoon up in a tree. Since he didn't have his gun with him, he just stood there grinning. Well, after a while that raccoon tumbled right off the branch and fell down at his feet. That's how he got his famous coonskin cap without firing a shot.

90

SECOND STORYTELLER. But he didn't grin to make people do what he wanted. Davy Crockett was friendly. He was good to everyone. People and animals all loved him.

FIRST STORYTELLER. You know, he always said he had just as many friends among animals as he did among people. Those animals weren't all tame, either. Some of them were wild. Many were animals he'd rescued when they were in trouble, and they never forgot his kindness.

Two of his friends, Death Hug, his bear, and Mississippi, his pet alligator, stayed with him all his life. He brought them up from tiny little creatures, and there wasn't anything they wouldn't do for him. He used to ride on their backs just the way he'd ride his horse, and with a bear and a horse and an alligator there wasn't much of any place he couldn't go.

SECOND STORYTELLER. There was the time he rode over Niagara Falls.

FIRST STORYTELLER. That was exciting. Davy Crockett and Death Hug and Mississippi were all out ice skating that day . . .

CROCKETT. Good skatin' here on this ice, Death Hug.

DEATH HUG. (*With great appreciation*) Gr-r-r-r!

91

CROCKETT. What about you, Mississippi? I know you don't like this cold weather, but don't you like skatin' around here above the falls?

MISSISSIPPI. (*With appreciation*) Cro-cro-cro!

CROCKETT. Wouldn't be safe Down South, but up here the ice is so thick you can cut any figures you please. Watch out, Mississippi, here I come!

SOUND. *Skates gliding swiftly over smooth ice.*

CROCKETT. How's that for a figure eight? Let's see you do one!

DEATH HUG. (*With great delight as he skates*) Gr-r-r-r!

MISSISSIPPI. (*As if he were enjoying himself*) Cro-cro-cro!

CROCKETT. Good! You're both better skaters than most people I know. Now let's all take hands and go around together.

92

DEATH HUG. (*In sudden excitement and fear*) Gr-r-r-r!

CROCKETT. What's the matter, Death Hug? You aren't afraid, a big bear like you?

DEATH HUG. (*As if warning of great danger*) Gr-r-r!

CROCKETT. Oh, I see what it's all about! There's a crack in the ice, and it's gettin' wider and wider—why, it's broken off! Now we are in a pickle. We have to do some quick thinkin', or we'll go right down over the falls!

DEATH HUG. (*In excitement*) Gr-r-r!

CROCKETT. All right. I'm a-holdin' on, so let's go!

SOUND. *A whistling noise as they go over the falls and into the gorge.*

93

CROCKETT. Good for you, Death Hug! Right down over the falls on that old cake of ice, and we didn't even get so much as a ducking!

FIRST STORYTELLER. Yes, he had lots of fun and lots of adventures. The best happened one winter morning when Davy Crockett was an old man. It was so cold when he crawled out from under his panther's skin that he couldn't get so much as a spark from the tinder in the tinderbox. And the daylight—well, it was so far from coming that Davy thought the dawn had frozen in its tracks. He decided he'd better start moving, so he put on his coonskin cap, found a stick for a cane, and called his dog, Rattler, to come for a walk.

CROCKETT. (*A weak whistle fading away*) Can't get my lips to pucker up and whistle, and that's

94

never happened before. (*Weak whistle again fading away*) Well, here we are anyway, up to the top of Daybreak Hill and just as cold as when we started. Rattler, what did you find over there?

RATTLER. (*Sniffing at a large mound of fur*) Arf! Arf!

CROCKETT. Well, if it isn't a poor old grizzly bear that froze to death. I'll put him on my back and take him home. (*Grunting*) There we are. Now let's keep a-walkin'. (*Puckering up and trying to whistle in surprise*) Hello there! Rattler, you see what I see? It's the cause of all this trouble. The old earth has frozen on her axis and can't turn around! Now what do you think of that?

RATTLER. Arf! Arf!

CROCKETT. And that's not all. The sun's jammed between two cakes of ice under the wheels! The more he has tried to get loose, the stiffer he has frozen.

RATTLER. Gr-r-r-r!

CROCKETT. Don't growl at him. He can't help it any more'n you could. This is a real pickle. Wait, I have an idea! I'll just squeeze the oil out of this old grizzly on my back (*grunting*)—and pour it over the sun's face (*grunting again*)—and give the cog wheels a kick—and there she goes!

95

SOUND. *The axis motor begins to throb.*

CROCKETT. The sun's loose, and the earth's started to move. That's all right, Mr. Earth. I'll just put a piece of the sunrise in my pocket and get along home. I can cook one of my bear steaks with it—and there's no doubt now that it's morning.

FIRST STORYTELLER. No, there wasn't, and the people all along the way thanked Davy Crockett for starting the earth a-turning. Davy just went along home, with the sunrise in his pocket.

SECOND STORYTELLER. Well, Davy Crockett didn't live much longer after that, but he left his mark on the people of his time and those that came after him. Sure, he told some tall tales, and he was different from the rest, but he never said a mean word. He loved every living creature. His country came first with him always, and that's why we think of him as one of our heroes today.

Yes, Davy Crockett was a great man. Some say, a giant.

MUSIC. *Played softly for a few minutes.*

*Nellie McCaslin*

## Paul's Great Flapjack Griddle

When Paul Bunyan finished logging off the woods of New England, he went to the Dakotas. He took along his crew of loggers and both Babe and Willie, the Big and Little Blue Ox.

In case you haven't heard of Paul Bunyan, he was the greatest lumberjack that ever lived. Some say he invented logging. He was of enormous size, with curly black hair, which he combed with a crosscut saw and brushed with a young pine tree pulled up by the roots. Ninety-seven ax handles would just barely measure him from hip to hip.

Well, it was on the banks of the Red River of the North that Paul set up his camp when he got to the Dakotas. He had so many men in camp that one of his bunkhouses had a hundred thirty-seven rows of bunks, built one on top of the other. The men used balloons to go up to bed and parachutes to come down in the morning.

They would pour out of their bunks just as the cooks were getting breakfast. It was a pretty sight to see them floating down with the parachutes, which looked like great clouds above them.

No loud breakfast gongs were needed in Paul's camp. He knew lumberjacks pretty well, Paul did.

98

So he just had a big pipe stretched from the cookhouse to the bunkhouses and a blower fixed in it. When the cooks had their fires going, the food beginning to cook, and the coffee boiling, the blower fan was turned on. The wonderful smell of breakfast was blown right into the bunkhouses. No gong ever brought men to breakfast so fast.

Paul found that feeding his many men was quite a job. The hardest part of it was to give them all the flapjacks they wanted. That was their favorite food, and he liked to keep his helpers satisfied.

Paul worried for some time about the problem of getting enough flapjacks for his men. At last he ordered Big Ole to make him a huge griddle. This griddle was so big that the cooks had to grease it with telephone poles. On the ends of the poles they tied great bunches of flour sacks, soaked with bacon fat.

As more and more men kept coming to work for Paul, even this griddle soon became too small. Then he had his problem to settle all over again.

Someone at last told him where he could get a much bigger griddle to take the place of the one that was now outgrown. It was so enormous that he couldn't at first decide how to get it to camp.

Luckily it was perfectly round in shape, but it was so thick, when it stood on edge, that it made a track as wide as a wagon road. Though it was terribly hard to lift, Paul soon thought out a way to get it to the place where he wanted it.

He and Ole made two big, strong magnets. When they were tested out for the first time, they pulled the axes, saws, and other tools out of the hands of all the lumberjacks within five miles of the camp.

Then Paul harnessed his mules, fixed his new magnets in the back of the wagon, and drove off to where the griddle was.

He swung the magnets around until their power pulled the griddle right up on its edge, and then he drove lippity-cut toward the camp.

The pull of the magnets got the griddle going around so fast and following him at such a great speed that he hardly knew how to stop it. The faster the mules went, just that much faster the griddle rolled along behind, trying to catch up.

At last Paul passed over the spot where he wanted the griddle. There he just dropped the magnets out of the wagon and pulled up to one side to watch what would happen.

The griddle rolled around and around, like a giant pie pan whirling about on the floor. As it got nearer and nearer to where the magnets lay, its rolling grew weaker and weaker.

Finally the griddle spun around a couple of times more, just at the place where Paul wanted it, and dug out a big hole in the ground as it turned. Then it settled down, as nicely as you please, right flat over the hole it had dug. There it was at last, all ready for use and with a place for the fire under it.

Paul then built a high fence around the griddle, and right beside it he put a couple of big buildings to hold his pancake flour. The buildings were so perfectly arranged that others just like them are used today as elevators for storing grain.

He also invented a machine for mixing the flapjack batter. He had Ole make ten of these machines and place them in position by the griddle. These machines of Paul's are likewise copied today, only on a small scale. Anyone may see these somewhat smaller models being used for mixing concrete.

"There now," said Paul to Sourdough Sam, the head baker of the camp. "There is a griddle to be proud of—a griddle which should be a delight to work with. Everything is nice and handy, and there is plenty of room for work. From now on, you should find making flapjacks as interesting as making your sourdough bread."

102

Sam was doubtful, for he had had several unhappy adventures with flapjacks in the past. According to Sam, his huge mixing pot had once burst and flooded the land for miles around with thin and sticky flapjack batter. He was not at all sure about the safety of making hot cakes on the enormous plan which Paul had just arranged.

However, after he got used to the new setup, he began to get interested in the business of flapjack-making. It was not long until he was turning out his giant hot cakes as eagerly as he made sourdough bread.

From that time on, Sam's flapjacks were so wonderful that men still talk about them. Covered with butter and brown sugar or molasses, they were the best that any flapjack maker ever made.

It was a wonderful sight to see the big griddle being put to its daily use. Along in the afternoon three hundred flapjack cooks would get down the flour and fixings from the elevators. Then they would start the mixers to chugging and stir up the batter under the watchful eye of the boss baker.

While the batter was being mixed, a whole troop of cook boys would grease the griddle. This they did by fastening sides of bacon on their feet and skating around over the hot surface.

103

When the batter was all ready and the greasing done, someone on the edge would blow a whistle. The griddle was so big that it took four minutes for the sound to get across. At the signal a cook would open the chute from the mixers, and out would roll a wave of flapjack batter ten feet high.

Paul had a hard time at first finding a way to flip the flapjack over onto its other side so that both sides of it would be cooked the same.

Everyone has, of course, seen flapjacks flipped up in the air out of a griddle, so that when they come down, they have turned over. In this way the undone side has a chance to get browned in its turn. Of course, the big griddle and the flapjack on it were far too heavy to be flipped in the usual way. So for a while everybody had to be satisfied with flapjacks that were done only on one side.

Paul tried fixing up ropes and pulleys for turning the big hot cake, but the pulleys weren't strong enough, and he gave up that plan.

At last he found a way to flip the flapjacks over that really worked. Whenever one side of the flapjack was done, Paul would explode a ton or so of dynamite under it. Away up in the air the big cake would sail until it was almost completely out of sight.

104

By putting a few more sticks under one side than under the other, he made sure that it would turn over while in the air. And he knew just how much dynamite to explode each time so that when the flapjack came down, it landed exactly on the griddle with the brown side uppermost.

After this, Paul's men never had any cause for growling about the flapjacks in the Red River Camp.

*Wallace Wadsworth*

105

# A Tiger's Tale

There was an ancient Grecian boy
Who played upon the fiddle,
Sometimes high, sometimes low,
Sometimes in the middle;
And all day long beneath the shade
He lunched on prunes and marmalade;
But what the tunes were which he played
   Is certainly a riddle.

Three tigers, gaunt and ravenous,
Came from the gloomy wood,
Intent to slay the fiddler,
But his music was too good;
So round about him once they filed,
Till by the melody beguiled,
They sat them softly down and smiled,
As only tigers could.

106

And thus beguiled, the tigers smiled
Throughout the livelong day
Until, at length, there was not left
Another tune to play.

What happened then I do not know
I was not there to see.
But when a man runs short on tunes,
*Can* tigers be appeased with prunes,
Or marmalade and silver spoons?
That's what perplexes me.

*John Bennett*

# The Lion

The lion is a kingly beast.
He likes a Hindu for a feast.
And if no Hindu he can get,
The lion-family is upset.

He cuffs his wife and bites her ears
Till she is nearly moved to tears.
Then some explorer finds the den
And all is family peace again.

*Vachel Lindsay*

# The Python

A Python I should not advise,—
It needs a doctor for its eyes,
   And has the measles yearly.
However, if you feel inclined
To get one (to improve your mind,
   And not from fashion merely),
Allow no music near its cage;
And when it flies into a rage,
   Chastise it most severely.

I had an Aunt in Yucatan
Who bought a Python from a man
   And kept it for a pet.
She died because she never knew
These simple little rules and few;—
   The snake is living yet.

*Hilaire Belloc*

# Wise Alois

Alois had always been a good boy. The teacher was proud of him; the minister was proud of him; but his parents were the proudest of all. Yes, Alois was very nice.

When he had grown into a lively young man, his father said to him at last, "Alois, my boy, the time has come for us to have a talk. You have a good mind, and a great future awaits you, I have no doubt. But you have learned all you can in our village school. You must now go and study in Basel."

"Yes, Father."

"I have put aside some money from the sale of a cow. Take it, and make good use of it."

"Thank you, Father."

A few days later, with the money safe in his belt and his best clothing in a bundle, Alois said good-by to his father and to his weeping mother.

At the end of the school year he came back to his parents for the summer vacation. They were very pleased to see him.

"How tall you have grown," said his mother, "but you are a little pale. You have studied too much."

"And did you learn many things?" asked his father.

"Yes, Father. I now know what the frogs say!"

"The frogs!"

"Yes, Father. I know what they say."

"So, after spending one year in school, and enough money to buy a cow, you have learned what the frogs say. My boy, if they teach you such nonsense at Basel, you'd better stay here and help us on the farm."

Alois went back to work on the farm. All summer, from sunrise to sunset, he helped his father. They first harvested the hay for the cattle, then the wheat for the bread. By the end of August, Alois had got back his brown, healthy look and felt ready for another school year. But his father said no. He asked his mother about it, and she asked her husband. He said no again, no, no, no, many times, but she kept on patiently, and in the end he said yes.

So, with some of his father's savings tucked safely in his belt, Alois went back to Basel.

At the end of the second school year Alois returned home. His mother kissed him, then said, "Dear Alois, you are as tall as your father now. Ah, but you are so pale again. You have spent too much time with your books."

"And what did those books teach you, my boy?" asked his father.

"Oh, Father, I now know what the dogs say!"

"Now look here, Alois."

"Yes, Father."

"No one cares what dogs and frogs say. Since you have been studying worthless books, you had better stay with us on the farm. This time I shall be firm about it. Very firm!"

Alois worked so well again the whole summer that when school time came around, his father felt better. After only a little begging from his wife, he took a number of crowns from his savings box and sent his son back to Basel.

111

At the end of the third school year Alois came home again. His mother kissed him tenderly, then said, "Truly, Alois, you are now taller than your father, but I shall be glad when you have finished with those dusty books. You are paler every year."

"Well, my son, you must be a scholar by now. What have you learned this year?"

"Father, I now know what the fish say!"

"Ah, that is going too far, my son!"

"Why, Father?"

"There is no future in it. I shall put an end to this before you learn what all the beasts of the earth say. You will stay here and be a farmer. That is all!"

So Alois went back to work on the farm, for good now, he feared.

Some time after that, on a warm August afternoon, Alois was working in his father's wheat field when two strangers came strolling up the lane. One was as fat as the other was thin.

"Oh, there!" shouted the fat man.

"What is it, gentlemen?" Alois asked, as he looked up from his work.

"What is your name?"

"Alois, sir."

112

"Very well, Alois. My friend and I are going
to Sion for the election of the president. Of course
we hope that one of us will be elected."

Both strangers winked, for each was sure that
he would be elected.

"I wish you the best of luck, gentlemen," Alois
said politely.

"Thank you, Alois, thank you," answered the
fat stranger. "Now you see, Alois, Sion is a long
way off, and while two are better than one for a
long trip, three would be merrier. You look like
an honest boy. Won't you join us?"

"We will pay your expenses," said the thin man, "and you can show us the way, which you must know better than we do."

"I know it very well, sir."

His father said that he might go, so Alois put on his Sunday suit and departed with the two strangers. These strangers were lively men who could talk of many things. They were so merry that the trip was like a party.

On the second day they stopped to eat their lunch at the edge of a green pond shaded by willow trees. The grass was smooth and fresh and invited one to rest. Alois enjoyed the food which his friends offered him, as well as their stories.

Suddenly he heard two voices behind him.

"I don't believe it," said one voice.

"Of course it is as you wish," said the other voice, "but it's true. It *is* a magic wafer."

"I still don't believe it."

"Who cares? And besides, if the minister knew it, he could save the old woman who is dying in the inn over there."

"Oh, you and your foolish stories! Good-by."

Splish! Splosh! heard Alois as he turned around and saw the legs of the first frog vanish into the pond. Nearby sat the second frog, still holding something in her mouth that looked like a round cracker. Alois kept to himself what he had heard.

The three companions stopped that night at the Inn of the Sitting Pig. This inn was quiet, as inns go. The servants spoke in whispers. As the friends came in, they saw the village minister coming down the stairs from the second floor.

"What a strange inn this is!" exclaimed the fat companion.

"Sh-h-h-h," scolded a servant. "Not so loud, sir. Our mistress is dying. She is in her apartment on the second floor. They say she will not live through the night."

"I can save your mistress," offered Alois.

"You! You never told us you were a doctor," said the thin companion.

"I'm not, but I heard what the frog said when we sat near the pond."

"Really?" The two companions stared at Alois as though he were out of his mind.

"Just wait for me."

Alois hurried back to the pond. It was almost dawn when he returned with the magic wafer, but the old woman was still alive. The minister, who stood by her bed, did not believe in the power of the wafer, but he saw nothing wrong about giving it to her.

It was a miracle.

116

Color came slowly back to the woman's cheeks. Life sparkled in her eyes again. She was cured!

A little later, feeling as good as new, she called the three companions to her bedside.

"Ask for whatever you wish," she said, "and I will give it to you if it is in my power to do so."

"Madam," said the fat and the thin companions, "thank our young friend here. He is the one who saved you."

"You are very kind, Madam," said Alois, "but all I want is three silver coins. It will be good to hear them jingle in my pocket."

So the woman gave him the coins, and the three companions went on their way more gaily than ever. They made the road seem short with their songs, and as they neared Sion they talked about the election.

The next night they came to a cheerful-looking inn which stood by the road. An iron chamois above the door showed it to be the Chamois Inn. Inside, a crowd of noisy peasants laughed amidst clouds of smoke.

"Where is the innkeeper?" shouted the fat companion, knocking on the table with his walking stick. "Come, come! Bring us your best food. We are three companions, hungry as wolves!"

He took the large piece of cheese which the
innkeeper brought, and held it between his knees
in front of the fire. As the surface of the cheese
that was nearest to the flames began to melt, he
scraped it up with a wooden spoon and spread
it on brown bread. This was the special dish of
that place, and he thought it fitting to enjoy it
before an election. Then the three companions
were shown to their bedroom where three beds
lay in a row.

Alas, they could not sleep. A large dog, right
below their window, kept howling tirelessly into
the night, while from somewhere far away, another
dog answered.

"Aren't dogs stupid!" the thin companion cried
impatiently. "I have often wondered why they
yell so for hours!"

"For no reason at all, you can be sure," growled his fat friend, "unless it be a cat mewing in the distance."

"You are wrong," said Alois. "These dogs talk with as much intelligence as we do. Moreover, what they are saying concerns us."

"What do they say, then?" asked his two friends. They had no doubts now that he was a great scholar, a learned man.

"They say there is a robber hiding inside the inn. At midnight he will open the door from the inside, and eleven of his helpers will then sneak in and rob us all."

"Mercy, save us! Is that true, Alois?"

"Animals never lie."

"Then we implore you, let's get help!"

The dogs were right. At midnight the inn door opened slowly, creaking, and eleven robbers crawled out of hiding, ready to sneak into the inn. At this moment a crowd of peasants fell upon them like a hive full of bees. They were struck from all sides by clubs, pitchforks, and brooms, and in no time were safely bound, hand and foot.

Alois became the hero of the night. When he said good-by to the peasants the next morning, his pockets were heavy with the silver coins the innkeeper had put in them. The fat and the thin man offered each other congratulations upon their wise choosing of a traveling companion. They sang all the more merrily as they tramped again along the road to Sion.

It was very dusty, however, and what with their singing, the companions' throats soon became terribly dry. They sighed with relief at the sight of a little brook which cut across a meadow. While they were lying flat on the grass, drinking the cool mountain water, Alois suddenly exclaimed, "Aha, someone's talking to us again!"

"Who?" asked his friends, looking about them. "We don't see anyone."

"That's because you haven't looked in the right place. You see the little fish over there, beside the big stone? The smaller one just said, 'You see these big men lying on their stomachs? They try to drink like cows, but they don't do it so well. They splash water all over their faces and coats. Well, anyway, one of them will be elected president at Sion.' "

Upon hearing this, the two friends were so delighted that they danced a jig by the stream.

"Aren't they foolish!" thought Alois. "One would think that two presidents were to be elected together."

The fish knew what they were talking about. The deeds of Alois were already known far and wide, even in Sion. When he arrived there next day with his friends, the people of the town were so proud to have him in their midst that they elected him president at once.

It is impossible to tell which one of the three companions was the most surprised. Anyway, the fat man and the thin man could not have looked happier if they had been elected themselves.

Alois sent for his parents so that they could share his good fortune.

"I always knew Alois had a great future," said his father.

*Roger Duvoisin*

121

# Things to Think About and Do

1. If the characters in the stories in this unit had been in a circus, what jobs might they have had? Which one would have been

the strong man?                    the mind reader?
the magician?                      the animal trainer?

2. What funny pictures do you see when you stop to think what the underlined words below really say?

Now we are in a pickle.
Can't get my lips to pucker up and whistle.
The land was flooded with sticky flapjack batter.
It was hard to give them enough flapjacks.

3. The following is an example of a little tall tale from "Paul's Great Flapjack Griddle."

Paul combed his curly black hair with a crosscut saw, and brushed it with a young pine tree.

How many other tall tales can you find in the story? Make a list of them to read aloud.

4. Change each of these "tall talk" statements to a plain statement. Which statement, "tall talk" or plain, do you like better? Explain your answer.

I can lick you with my little finger.
It was raining cats and dogs.

This story will curl your hair.
I was so scared my hair stood on end.
He can turn his bicycle on a dime.

Listen to your classmates talk. List the "tall talk" statements you hear them make.

5. Write your answer to each of these questions about the story characters.

Where did Paul Bunyan get the very big griddle?
How would the ability to talk with animals help the new president of Sion?
Why did Davy Crockett name his pet alligator Mississippi?
How did Davy Crockett cook his bear steak with a piece of sunrise?
How did Paul Bunyan travel from New England to the Dakotas?

6. Choose expressions to act out from one of the stories. Tell the name of the story, then let the group guess the expression you are acting. A suggestion from "With the Sunrise in His Pocket" is given below.

The ice is so thick you can cut any figure.

7. Make puppets of Alois and one of the animals told about in poems in this unit. Plan a funny conversation between Alois and the puppet, using ideas from the poems and from "Wise Alois."

123

# Some Books to Read

*Davy Crockett's Earthquake*, by William O. Steele.

Davy went hunting for bears, but he ran into a comet and an earthquake that changed the course of the Mississippi River.

*The Enormous Egg*, by Oliver Butterworth.

Exciting times in New Hampshire! Nate Twitchell's hen laid a huge egg out of which a baby dinosaur was hatched.

*The Giant*, by William Pène Du Bois.

A child giant whose handling is a great problem finds a friendly village where the people learn to love him. Pure nonsense and great fun.

*Little Witch*, by Anna Bennett.

Miniken Snickasee, the daughter of a witch, knows all sorts of magic tricks and uses them on her friends.

*The Enchanted Schoolhouse*, by Ruth Sawyer.

An Irish lad captures a leprechaun and carries him all the way to Maine in the family teapot.

*The Uninvited Donkey*, by Anne White.

Fra Diavolo, the donkey who is a movie star, upsets the Linian household. But they can not help loving her and laughing at her tricks.

*Jock's Castle*, by Katharine Gibson.

Jock and his dog, Sniffer, rescue a young hunter and win a castle as a reward.

124

# Important
# People

# Amelia Earhart

The four children had made the little roller coaster from boards and four wheels. The wheels had been taken from a pair of old roller skates. Skate wheels were small and rolled easily. The children were pleased with their work and excited about their first ride on this homemade roller coaster.

"Now where shall we start?" One of the girls looked around the back yard as she asked the question.

"The roof, of course," an older girl answered. "See how it slants down from the ridgepole." She was slender and golden-haired, a little taller than the others, and she seemed to be the leader.

"I'll be the first to try," she added.

"Be careful, Amelia!" the others cried. "You'll get hurt."

With a laugh and a toss of her head, Amelia climbed to the roof of the low shed. The others handed the coaster up to her.

On the first try, the roller coaster overturned. Car and driver landed upside down on the ground. The other children gasped, but Amelia got to her feet, unhurt, laughing harder than ever.

126

"I'm going to try again!" she said breathlessly.

This time Amelia took off like a bird, and there were no worried gasps from the others. She had landed at the track's end—right side up.

"Did you see?" she cried joyfully. "It's—why it's like flying! *I flew!*"

That was Amelia Earhart's first flight.

From the very beginning Amelia was different from other girls. The line under her picture in the school yearbook read, "The girl in brown who walks alone."

She was interested in airplanes and flying even when she was growing up. She spent much of her time after school at an airfield nearby, watching as planes landed and took off. Once she even took a course in engine repairing.

One day her father was with her as she stood watching a plane come in for a landing.

"Father," she whispered, "please go over and ask that man how long it takes to learn to fly and how much it costs."

It took five to ten hours and cost one thousand dollars!

At supper that night Amelia said, "I think I'll learn to fly."

"Good, when do you start?" asked her father teasingly. He did not think she was serious and besides he knew he could not pay a thousand dollars for lessons.

But Amelia was serious and she began earning money for lessons wherever she could.

Her skill and cleverness at the controls surprised the pilots who were teaching her. And finally with only ten hours of practice she made her first flight alone. After that she did as much flying as time and money would allow.

It was in 1928, when she was working at a settlement house in Boston, that a telephone call changed her whole life. She was invited to fly across the Atlantic in a plane called *The Friendship*. The pilot was Bill Stultz. Amelia would be the only woman member of the crew.

128

Amelia jumped at the chance to be the first woman to fly across the ocean and quickly agreed to go with Stultz. It took weeks to prepare the plane, but at last one morning at sunrise, Amelia and the crew left Boston Harbor to fly to Newfoundland. The take-off would be from there.

Today planes carry people back and forth across the Atlantic every day. When *The Friendship* made its successful flight, crossing the ocean by air was a great adventure. No woman had ever made such a flight before. Amelia Earhart needed a brave heart to climb aboard *The Friendship* for a flight that was to make her famous.

Flying, which had always been in her blood, now became her life. She was determined to set another record. She would be the first woman to fly the Atlantic Ocean alone!

129

On May 20, 1932, Amelia Earhart took off from Harbour Grace, Newfoundland. She had with her only the clothes on her back, some coffee and tomato juice to drink on the way, a comb, and a toothbrush. It was a long, lonely flight through hours of stormy weather.

In the record time of 13 hours and 30 minutes she landed in a pasture in Ireland. A surprised farmer ran up to welcome the lone birdwoman.

"Hello," said Amelia. "I've come from America."

For this flight the brave woman flyer was honored by other countries as well as her own. She was proving that women could do their share in breaking the ties that hold man to the earth.

From the time she made that flight to Ireland, her longing to explore the skies in a plane and set new records became even greater.

Amelia could not be earthbound for long. She was determined to prove that the highways of space belonged to women flyers as well as to men. She made many flights, across both land and water. Amelia Earhart was the first person to fly alone across the Pacific from Hawaii to North America.

"I have a feeling," she later told a friend, "that there is just one more good flight left in me. Anyway, when I have finished this job, I mean to give up long-distance flights."

The "one more good flight" was an around-the-world hop over the equator.

Like that first flight in the roller coaster years ago, Amelia's first try at an around-the-world flight was unsuccessful. She flew across the Pacific to Hawaii, but cracked up as she was taking off from Hawaii on the second lap of her trip.

In the spring of 1937 she started again, with Fred Noonan to steer their course. This time they left from Miami, flew across the Atlantic, across Africa, and on to New Guinea. On almost the last lap of the flight they took off from New Guinea for tiny Howland Island in the Pacific Ocean.

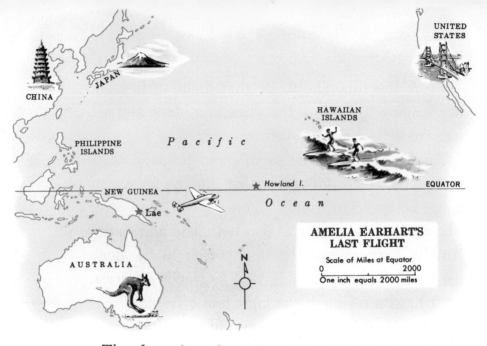

Map labels: UNITED STATES, CHINA, JAPAN, PHILIPPINE ISLANDS, *Pacific*, HAWAIIAN ISLANDS, NEW GUINEA, Howland I., EQUATOR, Lae, *Ocean*, AUSTRALIA, N

**AMELIA EARHART'S LAST FLIGHT**

Scale of Miles at Equator
0    2000
One inch equals 2000 miles

The day after the take-off for Howland a faint message was picked up by a Coast Guard cutter. Amelia Earhart and Fred Noonan were in trouble.

Though the Coast Guard and other ships searched the waters off Howland Island, nothing was ever found, not even a bit of the wrecked plane. Amelia Earhart had been right. This hop over the equator was to be her last flight.

The whole world was sad to lose America's brave woman flyer. But a bird cannot be happy anywhere except in the air, and everyone knew that Amelia Earhart had lived her life exactly as she wished to live it. This woman with wings wanted to conquer space. That was her life.

*Jay Strong*

# The Heroes of Yellow-Jack

"Yellow-Jack!" Fear gripped anyone who heard the words. That was the name that was often given to yellow fever. For two hundred years learned men had tried to find a way to prevent this sickness which swept through town and countryside in many parts of the world. Year after year thousands of people died of it.

What caused yellow fever? Some people said it was in the air around swamplands. Some believed that it came from tropical heat. Others thought it was carried on the clothing, the bedding, or anything else touched by a person with yellow fever. But these people were only guessing, for no one really knew how it started, or what to do about it.

Except one man—Dr. Carlos Finlay. In 1881 he said, "You are all wrong—yellow fever is carried by a mosquito."

No one believed Dr. Finlay until his theory was proved by a brave little group of doctors and soldiers about twenty years later.

The year was 1900. The Spanish-American War was over, but American soldiers were still stationed in Cuba, and many were ill with yellow fever. For this reason a group of army doctors was sent to Cuba to see what could be done. The leader of the group was Walter Reed.

The doctors visited sick soldiers and talked with doctors and nurses in the Cuban hospitals. They went into Cuban homes to check food and water, and to see how the people lived. Why did some people get yellow fever while others, living in the same house with them, did not?

134

Walter Reed and his helpers went to see Carlos Finlay and listened to him. Dr. Finlay told them, "A mosquito bites a person who has yellow fever. What does a mosquito do when he bites? He drinks the blood of the person he bites. Then he flies over to another person, who doesn't have yellow fever, and bites him. In this way he carries yellow fever from the sick person to the body of the well person. Nobody catches yellow fever by touching a person who has it, or by wearing his clothes, or by anything like that."

Dr. Finlay gave Walter Reed some eggs of the mosquitoes which he thought carried yellow fever. "Kill off these mosquitoes, and you will kill off yellow fever," he said.

This sounded like good sense to Walter Reed, but how could he prove it? He talked with other army doctors. They decided there was only one way to test the theory. They would let mosquitoes that had bitten yellow-fever patients bite well people.

Then up spoke two of the doctors, Jesse Lazear and James Carroll. "Try us!" they said. "Let mosquitoes that have bitten sick people bite us."

"You know what you are saying," said Dr. Reed. "You may die. You know there is no medicine to cure yellow fever, and that more than half of the people who get the disease do not recover."

"We will never know unless we try," they answered.

The first experiments were started on a hot August day. Eleven volunteers, including Jesse Lazear, James Carroll, and nine American soldiers, were bitten by mosquitoes which had already bitten patients with yellow fever. Only James Carroll and another volunteer got yellow fever and they both recovered.

About a month later Dr. Lazear was visiting a yellow-fever hospital. Suddenly a mosquito settled on the back of his hand, and he let it stay there until it had taken a good bite. Within a short time Jesse Lazear had died of yellow fever, one of the heroes in the war against the disease.

Now the doctors debated how best to prove without a doubt that Dr. Finlay's theory was right. Several experiments had to be made.

A camp, called Camp Lazear, was set up far from any town. Two little houses were built, with good screens on all the doors and windows so that no mosquitoes could possibly get in.

136

The doors and windows of one house were shut tight. The one room of the house was overheated and kept damp with tubs of steaming water. Bedding and pajamas that yellow-fever patients had used were brought in. These were shaken to fill the air with yellow-fever virus if it was carried on such things as bedding and clothing.

Into this house stepped three brave volunteers. For twenty days and nights they lived and slept there, wearing clothes taken from men who had yellow fever. Then they came out. Not one of them got yellow fever!

In order to be sure of the outcome of this part of the test, Walter Reed sent in other volunteers to do the same thing. The names of these brave men who were willing to undergo such a trial are unknown by most people. They were willing to die, in order to save the lives of others. But not one of the men who spent those terrible nights in that hot, dirty house got sick.

Now Walter Reed was ready for the next part of the test. The second little house was clean. It had one room divided in two with screening from floor to roof. Both sides were cool and airy but not a bit damp. Four men, two on each side of the room, slept here for two weeks. They stayed perfectly well and healthy.

Walter Reed removed the two men from one side of the room. Then he set free on that side, but not on the other, fifteen mosquitoes that had bitten yellow-fever patients. John J. Moran went into that space, which was filled with infected mosquitoes. He had just taken a bath, the bedding was spotless, and his pajamas were freshly washed. But waiting for him were the fifteen mosquitoes. They pounced upon and bit him at once.

On the other side of the dividing screen were the other young men, but no mosquitoes were allowed to get into their space. The two in the mosquito-free space stayed well, but Moran came down with a bad case of yellow fever.

In all, thirteen men at the camp were bitten by mosquitoes infected with yellow-fever virus. Ten of them came down with the disease. Luckily they all got well. So it was proved beyond any doubt that a certain kind of mosquito is the carrier of yellow fever and that the disease can best be controlled by taking measures to destroy the mosquitoes.

Now people knew what to do to prevent yellow fever—wipe out the fever-carrying mosquitoes! This was done so well that now there are almost no cases of yellow fever to be found in places where it was once a common cause of death. But let us never forget those brave men who, by risking their lives to find out how the fearful Yellow-Jack is spread, did a great service to the world.

*Joanna Strong*

139

## A Girl Who Loved the Stars

Except for one thing, Maria Mitchell seemed like any other young girl on Nantucket Island. She was one of a large family of brothers and sisters, and she had fun playing along the seashore when she wasn't helping her mother and big sister Sally at home. The one thing that made Maria different from her friends was her great interest in the starry sky. When other boys and girls were fast asleep in their beds, Maria would be sitting at her bedroom window, her eyes fastened on the stars.

Her father was interested in astronomy too. He owned a telescope and allowed his small daughter to use it. One of the things he did was to correct the chronometers of the sea captains who went out from Nantucket harbor on whaling ships.

A chronometer is a timepiece. It has a face and numbers from one to twelve, but it looks a little different from a regular clock. A ship's chronometer is one of the instruments a sailor uses to find his position on the sea. It must always be exactly right, or the ship might wander far off its course.

Whenever a chronometer was brought to Mr. Mitchell to be corrected, Maria was close at his side, watching all that he did. She longed to correct a chronometer all by herself someday.

Her chance did not come until the year 1832, when she was fourteen. Maria and her mother were busy in their Nantucket kitchen one morning when a knock sounded on the door.

"Mornin', ma'am!"

Mrs. Mitchell looked up quickly from her work. "Why, good morning, Captain," she said to the man standing in the doorway. "Come in."

Maria was busy polishing a kettle with sand. She stopped and turned to the doorway too. The captain was carrying a square box. Maria knew at once that the box was the captain's chronometer and needed correcting. Her black eyes flashed.

"Is William Mitchell at home?" the captain asked.

"No. He has gone to Boston," Mrs. Mitchell said. "He may be back tomorrow evening."

"Oh, ma'am, that's bad for me!" He looked at the box in his hands. "I must have my chronometer corrected. I'll need it by tomorrow morning, and William Mitchell is the only one on Nantucket Island who can do the job."

Maria knew how the captain depended on his chronometer to help tell where he was at sea. She knew it had to keep the right time. She went to him. "I'll do it," she said. "I'll correct thy chronometer for thee."

Maria and her family were Quakers and used the "plain" language, as they called it. They said "thee" and "thy" instead of "you" and "yours."

"Oh, I don't think thee should try that!" Mrs. Mitchell looked troubled.

The captain stared down at Maria in surprise. "A girl— just a little girl. Why, you can't be more than thirteen or fourteen. This is a man's job."

Maria looked the captain square in the eye.

"I was fourteen just three weeks ago on the first of August. I know how to correct chronometers. I've been helping Father do it for years. And I've been wanting a chance to do it all by myself."

"Well, well! Then maybe you can do it." The captain laughed. "Anyway, I can't do it myself, so it's worth a try." He put the chronometer on the table. "I'll come back for it tomorrow morning." He went out the door.

Sally had listened to Maria and the Captain while at work in the sitting room.

"Now thee will be in for it," she called to Maria. "Thee is sure to ruin the chronometer. Then what will the captain do?"

143

"I promise not to ruin it," Maria exclaimed.

"But thee has never done it alone. Didn't thee admit that?" asked Sally, as she came into the kitchen to argue with her sister.

"Yes."

"Then thee has no business trying when Father is not here. Mother, thee should not let her."

"Since the captain is willing, we should be," Mrs. Mitchell said quietly. "We know Maria is always working with Father. Maybe she has learned how to do it."

"I'll prove that I have!" Maria cried. "Just wait and see."

She wished it were night right away. To correct the captain's chronometer she would need to use another instrument, called a sextant, through which she viewed the stars. So Maria had to wait until the sky was filled with stars before she could begin work on the chronometer.

She finished the morning housework. Then she got the things ready that she would need that evening. She polished the mirrors on the sextant. She cleaned the little whale-oil lamp. Carefully she went over her plans for the evening's work.

It seemed the day would never end, but finally supper was over and the dishes washed. Still

144

Maria could not go outside. The kitchen must be in perfect order first. The plates and the teacups must be in exact rows on the shelves. Every chair must be placed just so against the wall.

Maria took one final look to see that all was done right. Then she made two trips to carry the sextant, the whale-oil lamp, and the chronometer from the house to the back yard.

She was glad it was a clear night. Eagerly she set to work. She adjusted the sextant and pointed its little telescope carefully at a star. She measured the height of the star. She looked at the time on the chronometer and wrote it down.

145

She set the telescope toward another star and measured its height. Carefully she went over every part of her work. She must be even more careful than Father, she told herself.

The night air grew cool. Maria was beginning to feel tired and sleepy, but still she worked. Mrs. Mitchell called from the back door. Maria didn't hear. Mother called again. "Maria, thee must come in. It's getting very late."

"Yes, yes, Mother, I'll be finished in just a little while now."

Not until she was sure she had done everything exactly right did Maria go inside to go to bed.

Next morning she was up at five o'clock. She stirred the fire in the sitting room, then sat down to do the figuring that was needed to correct the chronometer.

"This is the easiest part," she said happily.

When she had finished, she took the key and set the chronometer. She wrote the correction on a piece of paper to give to the captain so that he would know just what she had done. Then she put the paper and the chronometer where the younger children could not reach it.

Maria and Sally were both in the kitchen when the captain arrived. He looked worried.

Maria ran to get the chronometer. Excitedly she placed it with the paper in the captain's hands.

He looked carefully at the paper. His eyes fairly popped. "You've written the correction just as your father always does." His head nodded in wonder as he stared down at Maria. It was as if he couldn't believe that a fourteen-year-old girl had been able to do her father's work. "Are you sure you have it right?"

"Yes," Maria said.

"Well," he said at last, "it beats me." He took some silver pieces from his pocket and gave them to Maria. "Good day, ma'am." He bowed to her as he went out.

Maria saw that the money in her hand was just what Father was always paid.

How glad she was that Sally was there to hear everything! In triumph Maria asked teasingly, "What does thee have to say now, Miss Sally?"

There was a little smile at the corner of Sally's mouth and her eyebrows were raised. "Humph!" she said, "the chronometer must have been right all the time."

Maria laughed. "I knew thee would say something like that, Sally. How thee does hate to give in!"

Fame came to Maria when she was still a young woman. On the night of October 1, 1847 she was moving her telescope back and forth looking at the stars. Suddenly she stopped it. There near the North Star was something different. Maria knew where each star should be at this time of night. Here was something new. She thought it was a comet, but she couldn't be sure, it was so dim.

Quickly she wrote down the date and the time. Then she rushed to get her father.

One quick look, and Mr. Mitchell exclaimed, "Maria, it is a comet. Thee has discovered a new comet!"

The news flashed
around the world.
Astronomers in Europe had
seen the comet also, but none
had seen it so soon as Maria.
Her name became famous almost
overnight, and the comet was
called the Mitchell Comet in her honor.
Later, Maria Mitchell became the first teacher
of astronomy at Vassar College, the new college
for women. At Vassar she shared her knowledge
with other young women and helped them discover
the joy of exploring the starry sky. She proved
that women as well as men can be great astronomers.

*Grace Hathaway Melin*

149

# Stars

Alone in the night
  On a dark hill
With pines around me
  Spicy and still,

And a heaven full of stars
  Over my head,
White and topaz
  And misty red;

Myriads with beating
  Hearts of fire
That aeons
  Cannot vex or tire;

Up the dome of heaven
  Like a great hill,
I watch them marching
  Stately and still,

And I know that I
  Am honored to be
Witness
  Of so much majesty.

*Sara Teasdale*

# Henry Can Fix It

Henry lay on the cool green grass in the side yard. He was resting between jobs while he waited for the jug of spiced vinegar and water to take to the men in the hayfield.

"Ready, Henry!" called his mother from the kitchen door.

Henry Ford jumped up and walked toward the house. The green coolness of the grass felt pleasant against his bare feet.

"Tell your father dinner will be ready in about an hour," said his mother. "Is the jug too heavy?"

"No," he answered, taking the brown jug from her. "I can carry that, easy."

"If your father doesn't need you, come back. I need you to dig the potatoes, and then I have several errands for you."

To the ten-year-old boy it seemed as though there was work to do every hour of every day on the big farm. But there was time for good times too, sliding down the straw stacks, riding the horses, playing in the snow, and skating on the ice in the winter.

As Henry walked across the field, he thought how much easier life would be with machines to do the work and help bring in the crops. Still deep in thought he gave the jug to his father and started back toward the potato patch. Then he stopped and listened. In the distance he could hear the heavy chugging of a road engine coming from Detroit. He stood spellbound as the big machine came into sight. No horses were pulling it!

Henry raced to the fence to watch.

"G'morning, son!" shouted the man who was steering, as the huge engine came nearer Henry. He shook down the ashes and threw another shovel of coal into the firebox to build up more steam in the boiler. Then he asked kindly, "Want to take a good look at it?"

Henry nodded. "Yes, sir. I never saw an engine like this before."

The man seemed proud to show it. He explained how a chain was connected with the rear wheels.

152

The power of the steam made the chain move and then the wheels turned. The engine was used for driving threshing machines and sawmills.

Later, Henry told his parents, "A chain is connected with the wheels. Shift that, and the wagon stops while the engine's still running!"

His mother and father looked at each other. Henry was a born mechanic. He was far more interested in tools and machines than in animals or games or any of the things that most boys like. His mother smiled as she remembered all the nuts, washers, and other bits of machinery she had to take out of his pockets before washing his clothes.

The nearby blacksmith shop was Henry's favorite spot and he often stopped there after school. He knew how to heat the metal in the glowing forge and how to shape it on the anvil.

Henry liked to tinker with any kind of machinery. One of his friends, Will Bennett, showed him a watch as large and shiny as the one Henry's father owned.

"You mean it's yours?" asked Henry with awe.

"Sure. Granddad gave it to me. Promise not to drop it and you can hold it a minute."

Henry carefully reached for it. He held it up to his ear. "It's not even running!" He eyed it thoughtfully. "I'll bet I can fix it!"

The boys hurried into the shop. There was no screw driver small enough, so Henry made one from a nail. Then he began to take out the screws that held the works of the watch to the case.

"No, don't! You'll ruin it!" cried Will.

"Oh, it's all right." Just then the works dropped out, and Will Bennett groaned.

The cogs fell apart and the springs unwound. Henry smiled with delight. "I can fix this just like new. You'll see, Will."

It took hours, but finally Henry had the watch put back together again, adjusted, and running perfectly.

Through the course of the next few years, Henry took apart and put back together dozens of watches and clocks. At first he could not always

154

make them run, but by the time he was fifteen he had improved so that, with even the roughest tools, he could repair almost any watch.

There seemed to be little to hold Henry on the farm, for he had never liked it, and his father did not need him.

The little blacksmith shop with its forge and anvil had become too small for Henry's interests. The last work he did there was to build a small steam engine. He made it from bits of iron, pieces of wagon tires, broken bits off a threshing machine, and pieces of junk from a scrap pile.

When his engine was finished, Henry mounted it on an old wagon. He looked at it proudly. He sat at the throttle, blew the whistle, and rode lippity-cut across the meadow, frightening the cows that had been peacefully grazing there.

155

When Henry Ford was seventeen, he became an apprentice at an engine works in Detroit. There he learned more and more about machines. He read everything he could find on engineering, too, and long before his three years as apprentice were over, he had become a skilled worker at the plant.

By this time the people who knew Henry, both his friends and those he met only at work, respected his skill as a mechanic. "Let Henry fix it!" they would say when there was any trouble with machinery.

Henry went back home for several years to help manage the farm. His father gave him forty acres of land, some of it forested. Henry cut trees and sawed lumber for a house. He was going to be married, and he wanted to build a nice home for his wife.

Henry Ford's wife was an understanding person. She never lost her patience when he tinkered with machinery at all hours of the day and night.

"I feel sure that horses, with all the bother of caring for them and the expense of feeding them, do not earn their keep," he often said to Mrs. Ford. "One of these days I'm going to build a steam engine light enough to pull a wagon or a plow."

156

He finally was successful in building a small tractor. It had plenty of power and good control, but the boiler was a danger point. It worked under pressure, and sitting on a highly pressurized steam boiler was not exactly safe. So he gave up the idea of using steam after experimenting with it for two years.

After a few years of farming, the Fords moved to the city. There Henry was employed as an engineer by the Detroit Edison Company. It was about this time that gasoline engines were coming into use, and they were of great interest to Henry.

Now he had an idea for building a horseless carriage, and all the work he did for the next few years was with this idea in mind. Every free minute was spent in the workshop which he had set up in a shed behind his house.

When the neighbors heard the clang of metal and saw the lights in the shop as Henry worked late at night, they would say, "Poor Mrs. Ford, she has no life at all with that husband of hers! They never go anywhere, and they never have anyone in!"

Though she was homesick for their farm, Mrs. Ford was cheerful and patient. She knew that her husband would succeed.

One night she sat sewing until after midnight while he kept on working in the shop. At last, about three o'clock, Mrs. Ford went out to the shop. "Henry! You must come in. It's very late," she said.

"It's finished!" he exclaimed. "Just a minute, and you can watch it run!"

"Please wait until morning," she begged him. "It's pouring rain, and very dark."

Henry didn't answer. He was too busy hanging a lantern on what he called his gasoline buggy. Then he started the engine, climbed aboard, and drove out of the shed.

Suddenly it seemed to his watching wife that the yard had become full of many things. There were flower beds, a stack of flowerpots, the lawn swing, and a clothesline in the path of the little machine which, puffing and jerking, missed them all.

Above the noise of the engine came Henry's words, full of joy and triumph, "She runs! She runs!"

When Henry Ford drove his first car down the streets of Detroit, people acted as excited as if it were a circus. Many of them laughed at the funny gasoline buggy. Others were angry because it frightened the horses and blocked traffic.

"Ford, you'll have to get a license to run that horseless carriage," the police told him.

159

So the first automobile license in America was the one given to Henry Ford in 1893. He used this first car for a few weeks, then sold it for two hundred dollars. He already had some ideas for building a better car.

He went to work for himself in 1899. By that time there were other automobiles on the market, but they were so high-priced that only rich people could buy them.

"I will make a good car," said Henry Ford, "that working people can own."

He set up a company to do this in 1903. The first year he sold over seventeen hundred cars, but he thought his cars were high-priced too. He cut their price to six hundred dollars, and that year he sold over eight thousand. His factory went into mass production, and soon his cars were on every road in America. Production was so great that by 1929 about twenty million Fords had been sold. Today they are sold in every part of the world.

Henry Ford had a long and busy life. He often said, "A man must help himself. Success is always hard. To fail is easy. Do the thing that means the most good to the most people."

*Anne Tedlock Brooks*

# Victory

There was a young man
Who lived below
A mountain crowned
With glaciers and snow.

"Beautiful mountain,"
He used to say,
"Only the clouds
And the eagles know
Their way to the place
I intend to go.
The lofty peak
You lift so high
I've vowed to climb
Before I die."

When he was a man
He attempted it twice—
Bravely he scaled
Those shoulders of snow
And the arms of ice,
But for all his courage
The young man failed
In his enterprise

Then the mountain said
In his awful voice
Of glacier and ice,
"I am here alone
With the eagles and clouds,
And forever alone
I intend to remain."
"Beautiful mountain,"
The young man replied,
"I shall try it again."

So he started out
With all the gear
That people wear
When they try to scale
A mountain's crest,
And believe it or not,
He got to the top
Of Mount Everest.

*Mary Britton Miller*

# Mozart, the Wonder Boy

It seemed like any other January day in the little town of Salzburg, Austria. Housewives hurried back and forth on their errands, just as usual. And everyone talked about the weather, just as usual. There were a few people, to be sure, who knew that a baby boy had arrived at the house of Leopold Mozart. But babies were not unusual. It was a good thing, they agreed, that this second child was a son, since there was already a five-year-old daughter, Nannerl. But that was as much interest as they cared to take.

Certainly not one of the good citizens of Salzburg, except possibly the boy's own parents, could have guessed that this baby boy would make the twenty-seventh day of January a date to remember wherever music is loved.

"I wonder if he will be a musician," said Leopold Mozart as he gazed down at his new son. Leopold played the violin in the archbishop's orchestra and it was important to him that his son should like music.

"I think he will," Little Nannerl told him. "I want to be one."

Nannerl's real name was Anna Maria, but few people ever called her that. Wolfgang was the new baby's name but the family soon began calling him Wolferl.

Nannerl's words proved to be true. Almost from the cradle, little Wolferl showed a marked interest in music. When the members of the archbishop's orchestra came to practice their music with Leopold, the baby beat time with his little fists. He seemed happiest when the sound of violins and of the harpsichord filled the house.

When he was three years old, he stood one day beside the harpsicord while his sister practiced her new piece.

164

"Now let me play," he said when she had finished.

"You are much too little to play," Nannerl said.

Wolfgang paid no attention to her words. Climbing up beside her, he placed his small hands on the keyboard and played the piece more perfectly than she had done.

When this show of musical talent was reported to him, Leopold began to give his son lessons. Wolferl learned so easily that he astonished his father. One day when the friends had gathered to practice, the boy picked up a violin and played it perfectly, though he had never had a lesson on it.

Now Leopold was certain that his son was indeed unusually talented. He decided that Wolferl and Nannerl should give concerts together.

From the first these concerts proved a great success. Many royal families heard the children perform. Then, one day, they were asked to come to the palace in Vienna to play for the Emperor and his family. This was a great honor!

New clothes were at once ordered for the small musicians. They must look well for their trip to Vienna. This was easy, for both the children were beautiful. In the lovely costumes of that day, they made a pretty picture as they sat at the keyboard and played together. Wolferl was at this time about six years old.

166

When the great day arrived, the children drove with their father and mother to the palace gates. The Emperor and the Empress and their young daughter, the Grand Duchess Marie Antoinette, awaited the young musicians. The hall to which they were taken was a splendid one, hung with fine paintings and beautifully furnished. At one end sat the royal family. Wolferl and Nannerl were greeted kindly and then were asked to play.

First Wolferl played on the harpsichord and then Nannerl took her turn. Then, the two performed together to the delight of the listeners. The Empress invited the children to come to her side so that she could thank and praise them.

167

When it was time for the Mozarts to leave, they made their good-bys and started across the polished floor of the great room. Suddenly Wolferl felt his feet go out from under him and he slipped and fell to the shining floor. At once, the Grand Duchess Marie Antoinette was at his side, helping him to his feet.

Little Wolferl looked at the lovely duchess, about the age of Nannerl, and said seriously, "You are very kind. When I grow up, I will marry you."

Though Wolfgang amazed everyone by his ability to play musical instruments, it was as a composer that he won his lasting fame. From the time he was five years old, he showed unusual ability to write music. As the years went on, it began to seem like a miracle that so young a boy could compose so well.

He and his father now traveled through Europe and even crossed the water to England. There Wolfgang appeared before their majesties, the King and Queen. The British rulers praised his genius also. But all this attention did not spoil him. He continued to be gentle and friendly and loving no matter how many honors were showered upon him.

Once while in Rome, Wolfgang and his father went to hear a famous piece of music called the

168

*Miserere*. It had been composed many years before, and the music was owned by the Papal Choir. Only the Papal Choir had copies of it. To all others, the written notes were a secret.

Young Mozart, now fourteen, sat quietly, watching the conductor and listening, as the choir sang the *Miserere*. He listened to it with his heart as well as his ears. When the service was over he walked home and wrote the music perfectly just from hearing it the one time.

Leopold feared that the Pope would be angry when it was learned what Wolfgang had done. But when the Pope heard of the amazing deed, he honored the boy with the Order of the Golden Spur, an honor given only to the greatest men.

During the following years until his death in 1791, Mozart spent nearly all his time composing. He wrote many kinds of music.

It would not be possible to tell here how important Mozart's great genius is to the music of the world. Many books have been written about it. It is enough to say that wherever music is known and loved, Mozart is honored as one of the greatest musicians who ever lived.

*Doris Gates*

# History

All down the ages
Like a great tide,
Commoners walking
Where noblemen ride,
Now in the sunshine
And now in the shade,
People move onward
While History's made.

Churchmen make churches
And Lawyers make codes,
Builders make cities
And Romans make roads,
Soldiers make battles,
And Merchants make trade,
And people make changes
While History's made.

Craftsmen and Artists
Make manifold things,
Rulers make nations,
And nations make kings—
All down the ages
In great cavalcade,
People move onward,
And History's made.

*Eleanor Farjeon*

171

# Things to Think About and Do

1. Make a time line for the stories in this unit. Use paper cutouts or pictures from old magazines to show what happened or what was done by each person. Find out what other things were happening in the world at the same time. Add cutouts for these events to your time line.

2. Some phrases used when describing a great person are: (*a*) skill and knowledge; (*b*) courage and honesty; (*c*) willingness to work hard and not give up; (*d*) willingness to think of others.

Copy the names below and letter them to match the phrases that describe each person.

| | |
|---|---|
| John J. Moran | Maria Mitchell |
| Amelia Earhart | Henry Ford |
| Walter Reed | Wolfgang Mozart |

3. Who was of greatest help to each of these important persons, and how did the person help?

| | |
|---|---|
| Wolfgang Mozart | Maria Mitchell |
| Walter Reed | Henry Ford |

4. Show Amelia Earhart's four famous flights on a map of the world. Draw a different kind of dotted line for each flight. Give the date of each flight in a legend.

5. Paint a box to look like a book. On slips of paper write the name of a person, place, or thing that is important to the stories in this unit. Put the slips into the box. Let each member of your group draw one slip, read aloud what it says, tell which story it is from, and give a few important facts about it.

6. Write sentences using each word below with the name of a great person mentioned in this unit.

| | |
|---|---|
| production | appreciation |
| demonstration | congratulations |
| invention | correction |
| celebration | conversation |

7. Be able to complete the following statements by giving reasons.

The doctors in the Cuban hospitals were glad to talk with the army doctors because . . .

Maria Mitchell was employed to teach at Vassar College because . . .

Camp Lazear was built because . . .

Henry Ford made it possible for many Americans to own automobiles because . . .

8. Copy each heading below on your paper, then write the supporting details that tell about the main idea.

Mozart, the Boy Musician
Mozart, the Great Composer

# Some Books to Read

*Armed with Courage*, by May McNeer and Lynd K. Ward.

The lives of great people told as stories. Very beautiful pictures.

*Cartier Sails the St. Lawrence*, by Esther Averill.

Beautiful pictures add to this exciting story of Cartier and his adventures as he explored North America.

*Pioneer of Alaska Skies*, by Edna Walker Chandler and Barrett Willoughby.

An exciting story of a North Dakota boy whose dreams of flying with the wild geese came true in Alaska.

*Three Together*, by Lois Mills.

The story of the Wright brothers and their sister and how, working together as a family, they invented a flying machine.

*Young Hans Christian Andersen*, by Hedvig Collin.

The story of the shy, awkward boy who was often made fun of and laughed at, but later became honored and loved as a writer of fairy tales.

*Young Tom Edison*, by Sterling North.

Thomas Edison becomes a real person, kindly, and full of fun as well as energy in this story of his life.

174

Round
about
North
America

# Blower

Juan was the only boy who lived in the north end of Palomino Valley. He lived at the Sherman Grove Store, which was in the finest grove of oak trees in the valley. He had no father or mother and no one to look after him but the three old ladies who ran the store in the Sherman Grove Campgrounds.

Late one afternoon in July, Juan was in the kitchen helping Mrs. Maywood, one of the old ladies. Sherman Grove was empty except for a group of girl campers around the campfire pit. Suddenly Dave Plummer rushed in through the back door.

176

Dave had a small cattle ranch up on the mesa behind Sherman Grove. He was a tall, awkward-looking man, but the best horseman in all of Palomino Valley. He was always friendly to Juan. However this time he didn't even nod to him. He walked straight up to Mrs. Maywood and began talking very fast, his voice so low Juan could not hear all that was said.

Mrs. Maywood listened carefully. Her face took on a worried look. She shook her head, and Dave talked all the faster.

". . . but there's nobody else around, Mrs. Maywood," Juan heard Dave saying. "And that boy just naturally knows animals."

Mrs. Maywood shook her head again, and Dave talked all the harder.

". . . I can't say what might happen . . . and with all those little girls out there. . . ."

177

Juan saw Mrs. Maywood stop shaking her head. She looked seriously at Dave and said, "Well, you may be right, Dave, at that. It's up to the boy. You ask him."

Then Dave spoke directly to Juan. "Listen carefully," he said. "You don't have to do this if you don't want to. Nobody will think you're a baby if you don't do it. My red bull has wandered off the mesa, and he's out in the grove. I need somebody to help me corner him. Do you think you could get your horse and give me a hand?"

Juan looked straight up into the tall man's serious face, and he saw that this was no joking matter. Dave explained that he could catch the bull by himself, but he was afraid to chase him. If the bull got excited he might run into the group of girls and hurt one of them.

He thought that if two men on horseback could ride slowly and quietly up to the bull, one on each side of him, they could rope him before he noticed the girls.

There was no time to lose. The bull was wandering about loose in the grove, and he might be attracted by the girls' voices at any moment.

"If one of them should scream or try to run away, the bull might start after her," Dave explained.

Juan knew the bull. He called him Blower. Many times in the field at the edge of the canyon he had quietly watched Blower and had learned that he could not see well. The bull could not see him at all, even though he was only a few feet away, unless he moved or made some motion with his arms.

Juan found out, too, that Blower depended upon the wind to bring him the scent of anyone who was near him. As long as Juan was quiet and made sure that his scent did not reach Blower, the big animal would not know he was there.

"Well, how about it, son?" asked Dave once more.

"Yes, I'll help you," Juan said. "I'll get Moonlight, and . . ."

"All right, partner," interrupted Dave. "I'm going to ride up the orchard road a little way, then come back through the trees."

"Yes, sir," said Juan, his dark brown eyes shining with excitement. No one had ever called him "partner" before.

"Be careful," Dave said as he left. "Ride quietly and slowly, and above all don't scare him. Have your rope ready, and when we get the bull between us, I'll say, 'Now!' Then we'll both toss our ropes around his neck. Understand?"

"Yes, sir," said Juan. He darted out the door and ran to the small corral where Moonlight stood rubbing his back on a branch of twisted manzanita.

Quickly he saddled Moonlight and guided him past the manzanitas and the piñons, and up the road that led to the orchard. As he rode along he began to shake out his rope, getting it ready to use.

Juan turned off the road, and Moonlight picked his way slowly between the thick trunks of the oak trees. The sound of the horse's hoofs was softened by the deep carpet of old leaves.

Then between a pair of oak trees Juan saw Blower. The big red bull was standing with his head held up as though he were trying to make up his mind which way to go.

180

Juan saw Dave on his big brown horse talking to the leader of the girls. They were looking out through the trees and Dave was pointing.

The merry crowd of girls had been chattering happily as they sat around the big campfire pit. But they were quiet now and were looking too. Suddenly Juan heard an excited cry from one of them. He held his breath as he saw Blower wheel around in the direction of the noise. Then Blower started running with small, quick steps through the trees toward the campfire. Juan kicked Moonlight with his bare heels and guided him after the bull.

The sun was just going down behind Old Man's Mountain. It was dusk, a time of half-light and half-dark. The oaks threw spreading patches of jet black shadows on the ground. It was hard to tell which were the trees and which were the shadows. Moonlight stepped lightly but quickly across the ground. Juan could hear the loud snorting of the bull and the crackling of branches as Blower brushed against them. Once in a while he could see the bull between the trees.

Blower seemed to have changed his direction. Instead of running straight for the campfire, he was circling around to the left of it. Juan followed as closely as he could. He soon found himself in the road again, with Blower about forty feet away, turning back toward the campfire. Another one of the girls was crying now, and Juan knew that the sound was leading Blower right to the campfire pit again.

He stopped Moonlight and started shouting at the top of his voice, "Hey, Blower! Hey, Blower, come and catch me!"

The bull stopped in the middle of the road and turned his heavy head around in Juan's direction. Juan sat very still on Moonlight. Off to the right he could hear Dave's horse coming through the trees.

182

The frightened girls were standing close together. Each girl wanted to run, but their leader
had warned them to stay where they were and
to keep quiet.

Juan called again, "Come and catch me,
Blower!"

Just as it looked as if Blower might run after
Juan, one of the girls could stand still no longer.
She screamed and fled through the trees toward
the store. The other girls cried out for her to
come back, but she was so frightened, she just
kept running, screaming all the harder.

Attracted by the screams, Blower's head jerked around, and Juan knew that the bull could easily see the moving figure of the girl. Blower snorted, and his heavy body moved after the girl.

Juan yelled again, but Blower could not be tricked. His small, sharp hoofs thundered down the dusty road, a big cloud of dust rolling out behind him.

Without waiting to ask Dave, Juan thumped Moonlight's flanks with his heels as hard as he could and raced after the running bull.

The frightened girl left the road and ran into the last group of trees that lay between her and the store. Blower was almost upon her, and Juan was gaining on the bull. He knew he was not strong enough to stop Blower with the rope, even if he was lucky enough to drop it around the bull's neck.

So just when they neared the last oak tree, with a great shout Juan drove Moonlight crashing into the side of the snorting bull. Blower bellowed in rage.

184

The force of Moonlight crashing into him from the side caught Blower off balance, and made him fall heavily against the trunk of the tree.

Snorting and bellowing, Blower struggled to straighten himself. Again Juan forced the horse against the bull's side. His left leg was touching Blower's body, and Juan could feel the huge strength of the angry animal. Moonlight, his eyes rolling wildly, was fighting the bit and snorting fiercely, but he kept obeying Juan's knees.

As Blower got his balance a second time, Moonlight rushed him into the tree again. It all happened in a matter of seconds, but it gave the girl time to reach the safety of the porch. Just then Dave came riding up on the opposite side. Blower was still struggling and pawing the ground, but Dave swiftly and surely dropped his rope around the bull's neck.

"Use your rope, Juan!" he shouted, and he pulled his own rope until Juan could drop his over Blower's horns and back Moonlight away.

Blower snorted fiercely and pawed the dirt. The two riders backed their horses off and kept their ropes tight. They held the bull so that he could not run in either direction.

After a few minutes Blower knew he was caught. He still jerked his head back and forth angrily as though he would have liked to hook his horns into the horses. But he stopped trying to run, and when the two horsemen started riding slowly down the road, the bull followed.

Juan rode with Dave all the way to the Plummer ranch, where they led Blower into a pasture and closed the gate good and tight. Then, as Juan rolled up his rope, Dave put a kindly hand on the boy's arm.

"I'm proud of you, Juan," the cowboy said quietly. "You saved that girl's life."

Juan sat quietly in his saddle without saying anything. He was too happy to talk.

"Anything old Dave's got is yours, son. Put 'er there, cowboy!"

Dave stuck out his long, thin arm and shook hands with Juan. Then he rode off up the hill toward his little ranch house.

Juan walked Moonlight down the road to the store. As he watched a hawk circle in the evening sky, and the colors deepen into shades of blue and purple, Juan was glad the sun had set. He was so happy there were tears in his eyes, but he didn't want anyone to see a cowboy crying.

*Don and Betty Emblen*

187

# The Long Road West

Slowly came a cowboy riding round the night
   herd;
   Silver was the starlight, slender was the moon;
Then I heard him singing, lonely as a night bird,
   Pony's head a-nodding to the queer old tune:

"Wind, rain, and sunshine—every kind of weather;
   Sweating on the mesa, freezing on the crest;
Me and just my shadow, jogging on together,
   Jogging on together down the long road west."

Lazy was the cool stream slipping through the far
   light,
   Shadowing the buckthorn high along the hill,
When I heard a bird sing softly in the starlight,
   Singing in the evening when the trees were still:

"Valley, range, and high trail, mesa, butte, and
   river;
   Sun across the lowlands, rolling down to rest;
There'll always be the sky line, running on forever,
   Running on forever, down the long road west."

188                                   *Henry Herbert Knibbs*

# Saving the 559

Rip went another piece of paper—rip, rip! Pierre tossed the scraps away and sent his pencil whirling across the table.

His sister Marie looked up from her history book. "The School on Wheels will be here Monday, Pierre, and you won't have your homework done."

Pierre scowled. "I hate writing compositions," he said. "I never have anything to write about."

He reached over and turned off the big oil lamp on the table. Marie and he had worked right through a bad storm. Now the sun was shining again, and the lamplight was no longer needed.

Marie jumped up. "Maybe you can write about the storm," she said. "Let's go out and see if it did any damage." They left their schoolwork and ran to put on their boots.

189

Pierre and Marie went to a school that was not like any other school. Their schoolhouse was a railroad coach. In the bush country of northern Ontario where they lived there are no towns or villages. So a school coach travels on the railroad.

The coach stays on a siding at each place for just a few days. The schoolmaster lives in the coach with his family. The children come there, and the schoolmaster looks over the homework they have done and shows them how to go on with new work. Then the coach is coupled to a train and rolls on to another place. It returns several weeks later and the children go to school again.

Pierre and Marie were startled when they saw the damage the storm had done. Branches broken from trees were scattered everywhere. Great puddles of water lay all around, making the house look as if it were an island.

"There must have been a cloudburst," Pierre said, "right here in our valley."

"Do you think Father and Mother will be all right?" asked Marie.

"Of course," Pierre replied. "I don't think the storm hit anywhere except in this valley. Anyway, Father and Mother left so early they would be in town when it hit."

Then Marie cried, "Look, Pierre, over there! I see flashes. Is the storm coming back?"

Pierre looked in the direction that she pointed, and laughed excitedly. "That isn't a storm, Marie. That's Robert. He's sending us a message with his signal mirror."

"Oh, Pierre! What does he say?"

Slowly Pierre began to spell out Robert's message. "He says 'o-k-question mark.' He's asking if we are all right."

"Why, Pierre," Marie cried. "It's like having a telephone."

The signal mirrors were prizes which Pierre and Robert had won a few weeks ago in the school races. The schoolmaster's wife had shown them how to use the Morse code. This was the first time Robert had used his mirror to send a message across the valley.

Pierre took his signal mirror from his pocket and flashed slowly, "A-L-L O-K H-E-R-E T-H-A-N-K-S."

Robert flashed, "G-O-O-D."

Pierre signaled, "A-N-D Y-O-U-question mark."

The reply came back quickly. All was well at Robert's house. Then the sun went behind a cloud, and they had to stop.

Pierre put his mirror into his pocket. He said, 'Maybe we had better go see what happened to the cow. Father always does that after a storm.''

They sloshed across the wet, muddy ground. When they reached the field, they found the cow calmly chewing her cud. She had been wise enough to stay on high ground. It was a good thing too, for a big pine had fallen flat in the lower part of the field.

"We're lucky that it missed the cow," Pierre said. Then suddenly he remembered the railroad cut across the lower end of their land. "Maybe we had better look at the tracks, Marie," he said.

They hurried down to the railroad cut. There they found a small lake several feet long.

"Stay here, Marie," Pierre warned. He slid down the bank to the water.

The ground was soft. Mud and water sloshed underfoot. Pierre jumped quickly to where the ties should be. Bending down, he felt around in the water. Suddenly he knew something was wrong. The rails were fastened to the ties. They could be seen like two long pencil lines ruled straight through the water, but the bed of gravel and cinders under the ties was gone—*washed out!*

"Marie!" he shouted, "What day is it?" He had to be sure.

"Why, it's Saturday!" she called back. "You know, school starts on Monday."

Saturday! The day the 559 came through! His mind worked fast.

Engine No. 559 came pounding through every Saturday at noon. Along with her sixty-two cars of freight, she would be pulling two tank cars filled with oil for the Ontario mines. The engineer would know nothing of the storm. The train would come rolling downgrade and would hit the washout! There would be a wreck—a terrible wreck if the oil went up in flames!

193

"Marie!" Pierre shouted. "It's a washout! I'm going up the track to Hilltop station to stop the 559. You take the road to Fifty-Mile Siding and telephone the telegraph operator at Hilltop from there. It will take you longer, but I may not get through, and if the freight is late, he could stop it."

He started through the water, jumping from tie to tie.

"Oh, Pierre! Do be careful," Marie called, as she hurried off in the direction of Fifty-Mile Siding.

"Hurry, Marie!" he shouted back over his shoulder.

It was a long stride from tie to tie. The ties were wet and slippery. Some were covered with loose gravel. He almost fell. It was hard to hurry, but he had to. He had to reach Hilltop in time to stop the 559.

Once over the cut the going was better, and he started to run. The road twisted and turned as it climbed, and he couldn't see far ahead. Twice he fell, but picked himself up again. Would he be in time?

He thought of Marie, and he wondered if the road was safe. Maybe he shouldn't have sent her.

Then the track straightened. He could see the

Hilltop station now. The 559 had not arrived yet. He was in time. In his excitement he tripped, pitched forward, and rolled into the ditch.

Before he could scramble back to the track, he caught the sound. Sin-n-ng! Zin-n-ng! The steel rails were beginning to sing!

He leaped to his feet and saw the smoke of the 559 as the train was running into Hilltop. Now it was blowing for the station. Pierre looked at the semaphore. The arm of the semaphore was up, the signal that the road was clear. The train wasn't going to stop at Hilltop. He couldn't possibly make it in time now. He was too late.

He thought of waving, but he knew it wouldn't work. He had done that too often in greeting to the engineer.

Sing - -ng - -ng - -Zing - -ng - -ng! The 559 was picking up speed.

He must do something!

Words his father had said came to him, "When things get bad, your head is often better than your heels."

If only he had a telephone, he could warn the telegraph operator. A telephone! Suddenly Marie's words came to him, "It's just like a telephone."

Hurriedly he reached into his pocket and pulled out the signal mirror. Somehow he had to stop shaking, had to steady his nerves.

Sing-ng-ng! Zing-ng-ng! The 559 was leaving the station. It was picking up speed. The song of the rails grew louder every minute. If only the sun stayed out. He kept his eyes on the mirror.

196

SOS! SOS! SOS! He began to send the call for help. The engineer wouldn't understand, but the telegraph operator might—*if he were looking down the track!*

SOS! SOS! SOS! He kept the flash going.

The singing on the rails grew louder and louder! The 559 roared up to him. Gravel and cinders sprayed over him. He was lost in shadow. He looked up. He tried to shout. The engineer waved from the cab. The 559 roared on! He knew he had failed as the sunlight touched him again, but something made him keep flashing his message.

SOS! SOS! SOS! He had no hope left, but still he kept on, sending his signal after the train. It was the only thing he could do!

Suddenly there was a startling scream of brakes, and a terrible shudder ran through the whole train.

It was a moment before he understood. Then he knew. The 559 had stopped! It was saved! He felt himself shaking from head to foot.

A figure was swinging off the end car. He saw to his surprise that the car was not a caboose, but a passenger coach.

"Pierre!" a voice called. "Pierre, what's happened?" Pierre looked up into the schoolmaster's face. The School on Wheels had been coupled onto the freight!

"I was riding on the platform. I caught your signal and pulled the emergency cord. Pierre, what's wrong?"

Pierre told his story to his schoolmaster, the engineer, and the trainmen.

"It's lucky we hooked on the school car," someone said.

"It's lucky the boy kept at it," another said.

Pierre heard only the schoolmaster's voice. He was saying, "Fine work, lad! Fine work! Learning the Morse code paid."

Pierre himself was thinking of something else. He knew what he was going to write for his school composition on Monday. He had plenty to write about now.

*Zillah K. Macdonald*

198

# Homemade Fiddle

Almost everybody in that part of the mountains seemed to be jammed around the schoolhouse door. Irby could see the schoolmaster and some of the older boys inside, changing the benches around, turning the lamps up or down.

There were dogs, too, just plain dogs and hound dogs, slipping in and out between people's legs. And though some of them had collars, not one of them had more than fourteen spots. Irby had counted. Irby's dog, Billiam, of course, had twenty-three—twenty-four if you took in the little one at the end of his tail.

But a lot of the men had fiddles, sure-enough ones, not homemade, like Irby's.

Irby, silently fingering his tune on the two strings of his fiddle and trying not to forget it, wondered what it would be like to play on a sure-enough fiddle with all four strings. Irby had made his own fiddle and his own tune. He hoped he would win the third prize of fifty cents so that he could buy a collar for Billiam.

At last everyone was inside, and there was a scraping of boots, a squeaking of benches, and still more turning up and down of lamps.

Then Schoolmaster led old Fiddler up on the platform, and everybody clapped.

"I'm not playin' in the fiddlin' contest, folks," announced Fiddler. "Maybe ye heard I got married a short while back . . ."

That was all of forty years ago, thought Irby.

"And now my wife, she calls the tunes!"

People slapped their knees and laughed. The old man had to wait a bit before he could say, "But I'll show ye a bit of old-time fiddlin', just to start the judges off on the right track."

Picking up his fiddle, he swung into "Possum up a Gum Tree," and fine playing it was.

Irby, with Billiam sitting on his feet, found himself trying to finger the quickly whirling notes of "Possum" as though he were playing it to himself.

200

Then he jumped up, fell over Billiam, and dived for the door, because his own tune had gone clean out of his head! Suppose it didn't come back!

He hurried down the path, then out farther into the pines that edged the road, well away from the schoolhouse. There he stood still and tried to whistle his tune.

What came first? Oh, yes, the first few notes of "Turkey in the Straw," then the newsboy's call, repeated. Ah, now it was back again! Irby, still a little frightened, sat down on a stone and whistled his tune all through twice before he dared try it on the strings of his fiddle.

There were two other fiddles playing out there somewhere in the dark. So he wasn't the only one who was trying to keep a hold of his tune. When Irby finished, Billiam, who wasn't exactly a hound dog but always seemed to understand, sat down with a thump and a heavy sigh of relief.

As they sat there, waiting their turn, tune after tune floated from the lighted doorway of the schoolhouse. Irby recognized some that weren't new at all. The people liked them all right, you could hear that, but it wouldn't count with the judges.

There was one tune so slick and smooth it must have been borrowed from one of those radios. There was another that wasn't rightly a tune at all, nothing you could recognize or take a hold of and whistle. It was just notes played quick and one right after another, as you might repeat a lot of letters mixed up, but not making words or sense.

Irby and Billiam didn't mind these little scraps of tunes. They weren't loud enough to drive away the one in Irby's head. He was just beginning to find a new thing to worry about. Was it too cold out here for his fiddlestrings, compared with the way the schoolhouse would be heating up with all those people and those lamps?

Then someone came to the door and shouted, "Irby! Irby, where are you?"

Someone pulled him in the door. Someone else gave him a cheering tap and a push forward. His mother tried to slick his hair as he passed. Billiam trotted behind, letting on he wasn't scared

202

either, and stopping twice to growl, just to show people.

Fiddler had pulled Irby up to the platform, turned him round so he'd face all those folks down there, and was saying, "So here's Irby, and he's got a tune of his own for ye to listen to. It's brand-new now, but it won't be brand-new much longer, for I heard a redbird practicin' Irby's new tune the other mornin'. Looks as if he'd planned to take it on, once he learned his part better."

Everybody laughed except Irby. He was watching Fiddler for the signal to go ahead.

"Irby's got his own fiddle too. It's kind of a new thing, what he calls a knee fiddle."

Then he said in a whisper just low enough to reach Irby's ears, "Now, boy, sit down on that empty box, and don't lift your eyes off your dog until I tell ye to."

Irby put bow to fiddlestring and waited for the signal. Then he began to play, keeping his eyes on Billiam all the while.

Now he imagined himself on the steps of their own cabin with just Billiam in the dusty sunlight. The tune was coming quicker and clearer, with a marked beat, and his feet were keeping time against the worn boards of the steps.

There was a voice here and there out front, not more, though, than you'd hear coming up the valley on a still, hot day. Then, about halfway through, came a sound as if folks were beginning to pat their feet. Somewhere back in his mind Irby knew that folks were enjoying his tune. But he wouldn't look at the crowded schoolroom, because he knew if he did, his hands would begin to shake and the tune would just skid off into squeaks.

He repeated those few notes from "Turkey in the Straw" again, and stopped.

"Hi!" cried Fiddler to the folks listening but not yet beginning to clap. "How'd ye like that? Once again, boy," he shouted to Irby. "Once again, and I'll play the other part." He sounded excited.

204

It was hard for Irby to keep his tune, with the second going on. But—jumping jalopy, didn't it sound grand!

Scraping of feet! Benches were being pushed back to clear the floor for dancing. Irby still kept his eyes on that third spot from Billiam's left ear. Then he heard Fiddler say, "Wa-al, folks, if Schoolmaster says yes, Irby and I won't say no."

Folks began to dance. Again and again, over and over, Fiddler and Irby played Irby's tune. You couldn't help knowing, even if you didn't dare look up, that with all the dust and pounding, people were enjoying themselves. Why, the platform shook like the old wagon pulled across a dry stream bed!

Again and again they went through the tune.
Now Fiddler ran high up in the air with his part
of it, just as you could do on a sure-enough fiddle.
Then his part ran all round Irby's, in and out like
a dog driving sheep.

At last he heard Fiddler say, "One more and
we'll finish her, boys."

Irby's bow dropped from his tired fingers and
woke up Billiam. The judges, who should have
been on the platform all along, wiped their
foreheads with their big red handkerchiefs, left
their partners, and climbed back again. They
clapped Irby on his tired shoulders. They made
more speeches, but Irby could only hear his own
tune, with all those pretty bits Fiddler had done
on a sure-enough fiddle, going on and on.

While the speeches were being made, Irby even thought of trying to make a tune out of them, but he was too sleepy by now. There was talk of somebody who "will make a regular, old-time fiddler yet, when he's grown up."

Then Irby was almost awake again. One of the judges was whistling a scrap of his tune. Did that mean they'd got down to the third prize by now and that he stood a good chance for that fifty cents?

Instead, someone put a fiddle in his hand, a shining yellow fiddle, the wonderful kind you saw in the pictures in the mail-order catalogue. Maybe, thought Irby sleepily, they were wanting someone to hold it while the judges were choosing the winner.

Someone was passing round a hat—for Fiddler of course! They always did that when there was a dance.

That would mean it was all over, and he hadn't got his fifty cents after all. Billiam pressed closer, wagging his tail. Though he wasn't exactly a hound dog, he was mighty understanding, and he was trying to say that he wasn't disappointed. He could wait a little longer for that green dog collar that Irby had seen in the store window.

Now Fiddler was counting out coins—pennies, nickels, a whole silver dime—into Irby's hat. "Sixty-three cents," said Fiddler. "That's your share of the dance-music money."

Irby, still holding the yellow fiddle until someone came for it, gazed almost unbelieving at all that money. His money to share with Billiam, so Billiam could have his own collar with his name on it. Jumping jalopy!

Now he wanted to go home, to get right home, where he could tell Billiam and start writing out the wording he wanted on that dog collar.

"Who'll I give this fiddle to?" he asked.

"Nobody but yourself," Fiddler said.

Irby didn't understand.

"Ye gave 'em a new tune, didn't ye?" said Fiddler. "Wa-al, they gave ye a new fiddle."

Jumping jalopy!

*Erick Berry*

208

# Irby's Tune

## Tara's Burro

Tara lived in a tiny village on the shores of a lake, high in the mountains of Mexico. He was a Tarascan Indian. All the Tarascans were poor, but they were very proud. They worked hard to earn their living.

One day Tara was walking slowly toward the lake. Suddenly his face lighted, and his brown eyes danced with happiness. He saw his Uncle Lucio at work on a dugout boat at the edge of the lake. Lucio was Tara's hero. He was big and brown, and he had traveled much throughout Mexico. He knew all about everything. He knew how to build dugout canoes and how to take Tara fishing in them.

210

So now Tara ran toward the lake.

"What is it?" Lucio asked as the boy came up to him. "It seems to me that lately you have had something on your mind."

Though Lucio was so big and strong, still he was young and could remember the thoughts of a boy of eleven.

"Did you ever want something so much it hurt in here?" Tara put both hands over his stomach.

Lucio nodded. He always understood. "Tell me what this big want is that makes you hurt inside."

"I want a burro. A burro of my own. I want a burro so much that I feel sick with wanting."

"That is a big wish for a boy." Lucio stopped working to talk about this great problem. "Your father owns a burro. He lets you ride sometimes."

211

"But Toto is the family's. The burro I want must belong to me. He must be my very own."

Lucio nodded. "I know how you feel, but why must you have a burro of your own?"

"I want to go to faraway places. I want to ride over the whole world. I want to see everything there is. I even want to go to Mexico City."

Now Lucio threw back his head and laughed. It was a kind, not a hurting laugh.

"When I was a boy, I wanted to see the whole world, even Mexico City. I longed for something that would carry me even faster than a burro. I felt that I could not live until I owned a bicycle."

Tara's eyes widened. "Only the rich young men in Mexico own bicycles!" he exclaimed.

"I am not rich, yet I once owned a bicycle." Lucio's voice sounded proud. "I was much older than you are now, though."

"How did you get it?"

Lucio looked surprised at Tara's question. "Worked for it, of course. How else except by work does a Tarascan Indian get what he wants? We do not beg, nor do we steal."

Tara nodded. "But how did you earn so many pesos? It could take a lifetime to earn enough to buy a bicycle—even a burro."

212

Lucio laughed. "I am strong," he said. "I worked hard for many, many turns of the sun. On the coffee and banana plantations! Following the wooden plow after the oxen in the dusty fields! Bending over to plant the corn! Tramping the wheat! Anything I could do to earn a few pesos!

"At last I had enough to buy a bicycle from a friend who was tired of seeing the world. Then I set out to see everything, even Mexico City, and there, my restless one, is the world itself. You need go no farther. Everything is there."

Tara thought with longing of the wonders ahead that he must see someday.

One morning, not long after his talk with his Uncle Lucio, Tara picked up several *tortillas*, spread over them some of the bean sauce from the bowl on the back of the stone stove, and rolled them up. He put them in a cloth bag.

213

"I am taking a trip," he said.

His mother smiled at him. "Have a good time, my son," she said. She knew Tara would not be going very far.

Tara stepped from the dim coolness of the house into the hot sun. He started up the trail that climbed steadily to the hilltop. When it started downhill, Tara broke into a trot.

The sun was past the middle of the sky when he reached the big hacienda. It was very quiet there. Tara guessed that it was siesta time. He seated himself beside the big gate and took out his bag of *tortillas*.

Several burros grazed by the side of the road. Tara looked them over carefully. He decided that he would buy the one with the shiny dark coat. He was a strong-looking, beautiful animal. Tara could see himself on the burro's back riding toward high adventure.

214

"Who are you?" The words interrupted Tara's pleasant siesta.

He leaped to his feet and stared up at a tall man wearing a huge black sombrero.

"I—I came to work on El Rancho," Tara said. "I am a good worker. I must earn money to buy a burro. That one over there!" He pointed to the dark burro which in his mind he now owned.

The tall man in the huge sombrero, who was known as the boss, began to laugh. "José, come!" he shouted.

When one of his workers hurried to the gate, the boss said, "This boy wants to work on El Rancho. He must earn money to buy a burro."

215

José grinned and said, "He will be too old to ride a burro by the time he can earn enough pesos to buy one. Too young he is to do anything but herd goats."

"He wants Diablo over there." The boss began to laugh again.

"Oh, that one!" and José laughed too.

Tara was puzzled. What was so funny about a person's asking for work to buy himself a burro?

The boss looked at Tara. "Maybe you could help drive burros loaded with bananas to the big market."

Tara's heart leaped. "I could do that," he said.

"If you work well, you may be given the black burro as your pay. Be here at this gate at sunup."

Next morning Tara was back at the hacienda. Off in the field was the black burro, Diablo.

Soon José arrived and said, "Take a long stick and help keep the burros going. Keep them in the road. Get busy now."

Tara found a stick which would do to smack any stubborn burro. To his delight Tara saw that Diablo was going along with the banana train. Strangely enough, though, he carried no load.

"Why does my friend there carry no load?" Tara asked José, and pointed toward Diablo.

216

"He is too young to carry loads," José explained.

Tara talked to Diablo and told him what a special burro he was. In time the black burro took to following him around like a dog.

"What a smart burro he is," the boss said. "He knows that he is to belong to you."

The trip was long and tiring, but at last the big market was reached. Then Tara forgot his weariness in staring at the many sights. Never had he seen anything like it.

When the burro train got back to El Rancho, the owner was waiting.

"That Diablo! I see he's still with the herd. You haven't found out a way to outsmart him yet, José?" he asked.

"Yes, *señor*," José said. "The boss promised him to the boy over there for helping to drive the herd to the big market."

The owner laughed. "Big boss is smart," he said.

Tara was puzzled by these words.

The owner turned to Tara. "All right, boy, put a bridle on the black burro and ride him away. He's all yours."

"I give you my thanks, *señor*," Tara said.

José went to the barn with him and gave him a bridle. Diablo came at Tara's whistle, as he had learned to do on the long trip back from the big market. Tara and José had no trouble in slipping the bridle over the burro's head. Tara patted the shiny black neck and talked softly to Diablo before he threw himself onto the burro's back.

In no time at all, Tara found himself plunk on the ground with Diablo almost sitting in his lap. He picked himself up, hurt only because the workmen at El Rancho laughed. They had gathered round in a circle to watch.

"A fine way to act, Diablo!" Tara whispered in Diablo's ear.

Diablo raised his head and a great heehaw came from his mouth.

218

Tara took a better grip on the bridle rein and again climbed onto the stubborn burro's back. Again Diablo sat down, and Tara slid to the ground. He tried again, and again. Each time Diablo sat and Tara slid.

Angrily Tara picked himself up and started down the trail toward home. Diablo was right at his heels. Tara had a burro. But what a burro!

When he reached the village where he lived, everyone looked at Tara in surprise as he walked along with the black burro trotting at his heels.

"What a fine burro," his father cried, "but why are you not riding him?"

219

Tara hung his head and felt foolish. "I worked hard to earn a stubborn burro that I cannot ride," he said.

"Is that possible?" said his father, eyeing the burro. "Let us see you try."

Tara climbed onto Diablo's back. Diablo promptly sat down and Tara slid to the ground.

Tara picked himself up and shook his head sadly. "He does it every time," he said, but nobody laughed.

The next day Tara went down to the lake and told Lucio about his new problem. Of course the burro had followed at his heels.

Lucio went into the house and came out with some pieces of leather and rope. He went a short distance on a side hill and came back with two round and very prickly cacti. He then rigged up a sort of leather-and-rope harness, fastened the cacti inside, and put it on Diablo.

"Now get on," Lucio said, "and be ready to hang on tight."

Tara mounted and grabbed Diablo around the neck. He felt himself sliding as Diablo sat down, but suddenly with a loud heehaw of protest the burro was up. His heels kicked out three times, then with another snort he stood still.

220

"It worked," Lucio said. "Now give him a gentle kick with your heels. Make him go."

Tara did so, and Diablo stepped quietly forward.

"Stop!" Lucio said, taking hold of the bridle. "Now slide off and try it again."

Tara slid off, then mounted again. Diablo tried to sit down, but quickly jerked up to his four feet with a surprised snort, and Lucio led him forward.

Time after time they went through this act. At last Lucio gently removed the harness with the prickly cacti which had stuck Diablo whenever he tried to sit down. Maybe the burro did not know that the cacti had been removed, but he was taking no chances. He walked forward, as a good burro should.

Lucio rolled up the leather-and-rope harness with the prickly cacti inside. "Use this whenever Diablo feels like sitting," he said. "I don't think you'll have much more trouble with him. He's smart. He learns fast. You've got yourself a good and useful friend there."

"Thank you! Thank you!" Tara called happily. "No one ever had such an uncle as you."

Proudly he rode through the village. All the boys left their play to stare at him. Nobody laughed as he rode past with a wave of the hand. Diablo was a fine burro, a very fine burro.

*Shannon Garst*

222

# Burro with the Long Ears

*Ja-Nez*—burro with the long ears—
Come with me to the water hole.
I will fill the kegs with water
And you will carry them home.
Down the crooked trail,
Through the deep hot sand,
Past the fragrant piñon trees,
Winding this way, winding that way,
Do not step into the cactus.
Now I wade into the water
Where it is clearest; I dip and pour.
While you drink I fill the kegs.
They are heavy as I lift them to your back again.
Now we wander through the cactus,
Past the fragrant trees,
Up the sandy trail, winding slowly.
At the hogan my mother sees
Us coming home with water.

*Hilda Faunce Wetherill*
*(From the Navaho American Indian)*

223

# Gloucester Boy

When Manuel went on board his Uncle Joe's schooner, the twelve men of the crew were busy getting the boat ready to sail. The schooner's engine was already at work. People on the wharf were shouting good-bys. Some of Manuel's friends were among them, watching as the schooner slowly left the port of Gloucester and nosed her way out to Eastern Point.

Uncle Joe had said, "It's a man's work to go dragging for fish, but the cook can use a lively boy in the galley, and that's a good way to start out on a fishing boat when you're young."

That's why Manuel went right down to the galley. He was eager to learn what Tony, the cook, expected him to do. Tony put him to work peeling potatoes and other vegetables and getting the table ready for dinner.

224

Manuel wondered at the high-priced food he saw being cooked.

"Is every meal so good, like a feast?" he asked when Tony took a number of steaks from the refrigerator.

"Ha!" replied Tony, "best food on earth isn't too good for fishermen. When you see how they work and keep going without sleep and rest, you will know that they need good food, and nothing is as good as a fine steak."

225

The days they were on the way to the Banks seemed long and quiet to Manuel. But the morning Uncle Joe threw out the sounding lead, a very different feeling came upon everyone. How Manuel wished he could swing out the sounding lead with the grand swing his uncle had! But Captain Joe told him there was a trick to it, and if he didn't know how to do it, his arm might get caught in the cord and badly hurt.

Breathlessly the lead was studied, for the kind of stuff sticking to it would show exactly what sort of fishing ground was below.

Again the lead was dropped, and this time the men sprang into action at once. It was time to throw out the nets. Heavy iron weights, called doors, were attached to the great net at each side. As they went overboard, the net, with its glass floats to keep it spread apart, sank swiftly.

"How far down will it go?" asked Manuel, watching the place where it sank.

"Maybe fifteen fathoms. The cod that we want stay within three fathoms of the bottom," said Captain Joe.

Manuel knew that a fathom is six feet. "But how do you know it's cod down there?" he exclaimed.

226

"The lead showed us that. We know, from long years of fishing, just what fish belong to certain kinds of sea bottom."

The engineer, who was called the chief, was in charge of the machine used for lifting the net. As it was dragged close to the schooner, the doors heaved up, and the net, alive with wiggling fish, came into sight. In no time the fish were dumped into the open hatches, and one of the crew shoveled ice between the layers as fast as they came down.

"Heave her out again!" commanded Captain Joe.

The net went overboard again, and the schooner went ahead. Manuel began to wonder why Tony did not give him any orders for kitchen duty. He was hungry, but no one paid any attention to being hungry, it seemed. Even Tony was working on deck. The net went over again, and the cod were dumped again and again into the hatches.

Manuel went below and cut some bread and made a pile of sandwiches. He brought them up and handed them around to the crew, who stuffed them into their mouths but kept their eyes on the net.

"Uncle Joe!" Manuel pushed a sandwich under his nose. He gobbled it down as if he did not know what he was doing.

Tony gave Manuel a grin and said, "Good boy. Make some coffee, eh?"

Manuel made coffee, and watched while each man managed to gulp a cup of the steaming drink.

Then Manuel went below and cleaned up the galley. Afterward he sat on his bunk and suddenly fell asleep. How long he slept he did not know. He awoke to hear the thud of feet, the shouted orders, the squeak of the machine pulling in the net, and he went on deck to see the same sight he had left hours before. The men were weary but happy, for their luck was holding out.

Manuel knew now why such high boots were needed, for the deck was wet and sloshy, and only oilskins kept the men dry. There was a cold, salty smell in the air, and as the last net came up with only a small catch, Captain Joe called, "Guess we cleaned up this ground all right."

Soon half the crew were asleep, the other half on watch as it grew dark. Tony hustled Manuel around as he had never been hustled before. The best food on hand was brought out, and tired, aching fishermen ate as if they were starved.

229

"Hi, Manuel!" yelled the chief. "That was a good idea of yours to bring up sandwiches and coffee. Hope you sign up for good."

"In a few years I'll be old enough to sign up for good," Manuel replied, grinning with delight.

The next day was cold, and Manuel went below to warm up and listen to the radio for market reports of fish prices at the Boston pier. The names of the boats, how many thousand pounds of fish they sold, and the prices were being told by the announcer. Then came the weather report.

"Northeast storm warnings from Eastport to Block Island. Forty-mile northeast winds, increasing along the coast today."

At once Manuel went up to Captain Joe and repeated the announcer's words.

"Listen to the next report. We must get all the fish we can before that storm breaks."

Manuel, like a good seaman, obeyed at once. Again the warning came that the northeast winds would increase. At the same time there was a change in the motion of the schooner.

Manuel raced up the steep ladder and found the men dragging in a full net, the water pouring over the decks, fish slipping into the hatches, ice being shoveled over them. The holds were full.

230

"Batten down the hatches!" cried Captain Joe.

The weary men bent over their duties and worked like mad, tightening the hatches.

"Are we going to make for a port, Uncle Joe?" asked Manuel.

"Ha! We ride out the storm right. here, not near the reefs," he answered. "To make port would be dangerous. The sea is rougher close to the shore, where it is shallower, you know."

Manuel did not know that. The engines ran full speed. The waves began to lift and wash across the deck. Rain fell, increasing the floods of water.

"Go below, Manuel, and stay there," ordered the captain with a sharp look.

231

Manuel felt the motion of the tossing schooner as the huge waves swept down on the deck. He grasped anything he could, to keep from being thrown overboard. He obeyed his orders, though, and crawled safely to the ladder and went below to sit in the forecastle. Some of the crew were already sound asleep. Nothing could keep them awake during their two hours off duty.

Tony was still on deck, and Manuel could think of no work to do. The forecastle was hot. He found it hard to remember how icy and sharp the winds were above. The schooner tossed and rolled like a chip on the mountainous waves. He wanted to go up again, but he remembered his orders.

Then he said to himself, "Maybe if I take just one look, Uncle Joe won't mind." He put on his heavy sweater but left his oilskins beside the bunk. Clutching the rail, he climbed up the ladder and through the little door at the top. For a moment he held fast to a line that hung from a mast and breathed the wild air.

Then, before any one of the crew busy on deck knew what was happening, a huge wave thundered over and swept Tony overboard with it. He tossed for a second on the water, but in his heavy fishing clothes he was helpless to save himself.

232

Like a flash, Manuel, remembering his lessons in lifesaving, kicked off his sea boots and dived overboard. Captain Joe threw out a line after him.

The crew watched breathlessly. They saw Manuel swim close to Tony, grab his coat collar in one hand, and reach for the line with the other.

Then Tony got his hand on the line, and someone began to pull it in with Tony holding fast to it. Manuel struggled to reach a second line which had been tossed out for him. For a while it bounced on the waves beyond his reach. When he finally grasped it, he was so cold he could hardly hold on to it.

Hours passed, it seemed to Manuel. Then he was on deck. He was carried below, undressed and tucked into his bunk. He sipped a cup of hot milk and soon he began to breathe naturally again. All at once he was fast asleep.

When Manuel awoke, the schooner was rocking gently. He opened his eyes wider, and there was Tony grinning from ear to ear at him.

"Ho! So you are awake at last, eh, boy?"

Manuel sat up with a start and it all came back to him. "Oh, Tony, I didn't obey my orders."

"Well, this time I guess the captain will let it go. He says it's a good thing the youngest member of the crew can swim. Maybe we should all learn. Me—I'm going to."

Tony had wrung out his wet clothes and had dry ones laid out for him. He was worrying over him as if he were the apple of his eye.

The schooner had been carried off her course while riding out the storm, and it took a day longer to get home. Manuel worked hard in the galley. The men were always hungry and tired after sixty hours of fishing, and the storm had added to their work. But the holds were full, and the radio reported good prices at the Boston fish pier. So they went there to sell their fish.

When at last they came into the port of Gloucester, Captain Joe called Manuel to him as he stood at the wheel.

"Hold the wheel while I light my pipe," he said. "You earned a share in the sale of the fish, Manuel. Shall we put your money in the bank?"

Manuel nodded yes. His thoughts were busy and happy.

"What are you thinking of?" asked the captain.

"I'll save the money to buy a schooner some-day," said Manuel.

235

The wheel felt wonderful in his hands. He looked proudly about the orderly deck and glanced up at the tall masts and full sails against the blue sky. He saw the gulls rise from the rocks to meet them. His eyes sparkled with the joy a captain feels as he brings his ship into port.

"You're a chip off the old block," laughed Captain Joe. Then as Eastern Point came into sight, he added softly, "A Gloucester boy, eh?"

*Ruth and Richard Holberg*

# The Sea Wolf

The fishermen say, when your catch is done
   And you're sculling in with the tide,
You must take great care that the Sea Wolf's share
   Is tossed to him overside.

The fishermen say, when it storms at night
   And the great seas bellow and roar,
That the Sea Wolf rides on the plunging tides,
   And you hear his howl at the door.

And you must throw open your door at once,
   And fling your catch to the waves,
Till he drags his share to his cold sea lair,
   Straight down to his salt sea caves.

Then the storm will pass, and the still stars shine,
   In peace—so the fishermen say—
But the Sea Wolf waits by the cold Sea Gates
   For the dawn of another day.

*Violet McDougal*

237

# Things to Think About and Do

1. With other members of your group, plan and write the front page of a newspaper. Decide which events in the stories in this unit are front-page news. Each member of the group might write the story of one event. Make the headlines interesting.

2. Write Pierre's composition as you think he would have written it. Marie had a different story to tell. Write her composition also.

3. Like Tara, have you had a big want that made you hurt inside? Plan to tell about your big want, how you got it, or how you learned to do without it, or about something that took its place.

4. Be prepared to explain the following as they are used in the stories in this unit.

> In the bush country. . . .
> "A Gloucester boy, eh?"
> . . . a chip off the old block.
> The coach stays on a siding.
> . . . as if he were the apple of his eye.
> Tara guessed that it was siesta time.
> . . . on the way to the Banks. . . .

5. Make a chart to show how Juan's big oak trees compare with other big trees, such as redwoods, Douglas firs, etc. Use the encyclopedia and other

books to find where each kind grows, its possible height and age, the thickness of the trunk, whether the wood is hard or soft and how it is used.

6. The language in the statements below is like that spoken by some people in the places where four of the stories in this unit take place. Name the place and the story for each statement.

"Is every meal so good, like a feast?"
"There, my restless one, is the world itself."
"Put 'er there, cowboy!"
"But I'll show ye a bit. . . ."
". . . for many, many turns of the sun."

Which story was left out? Why?

7. Explain each of the old sayings below. Why might Pierre's father have used them to teach Pierre what to do when things get bad?

Nothing is done with a leap.
A spur in the head is worth two in the heels.
Who falls short in the head must be long in the heels.
Look before you leap.

8. What sentence on page 205 of "Homemade Fiddle" makes a word picture by comparing one thing with another? What two things are compared? Skim the stories in this unit for other word pictures that are made by comparing.

# Some Books to Read

*Sea Pup*, by Archie Binns.

Clint and his pet seal have a fight with killer whales while sailing in the Puget Sound area.

*The Golden Bird*, by Shannon Garst.

The further adventures of Tara, the Mexican Indian boy you met in the story called "Tara's Burro."

*Juddie*, by Florence Wightman Rowland.

Juddie longs to go to school, but he is needed to help with the work on the family farm in Canada.

*Miracles on Maple Hill*, by Virginia Sorensen.

An exciting story of a year of surprises and miracles on grandmother's Pennsylvania farm.

*Prairie School*, by Lois Lenski.

The South Dakota wheat country is the setting for this story of children and teacher marooned in the country school during a blizzard.

*Whitey and the Wild Horse*, by Glen Rounds.

Two children of the Western plains capture and hide a wild horse.

*Minn of the Mississippi*, by Holling C. Holling.

A three-legged snapping turtle explores the great river from Canada to the Gulf of Mexico. Wonderful pictures.

# When Roads Led West

# Lost Boy

The early morning sunlight brightened the doorway of the little cabin where Cale was standing with his mother and his little brother Verygood. Cale was ready to start on the four-mile walk to the clearing where Father was cutting trees for a new home.

Five-year-old Verygood gave an excited little bounce. "May I go too, Mother?" he asked.

Mother smiled. "It's a long way for a small boy to walk, and last evening thee was so tired from play thee couldn't eat thy supper. If thee stays home today, thy sisters will play Up Flies the Dove with thee. Lyddy and Betsey are washing clothes now, but they won't be busy all day."

242

"Up Flies the Dove," echoed Verygood, laughing. Then he frowned. "But my father wants to see me."

Mother laughed. "I can't stand here arguing with thee all day. Cale, take good care of thy little brother."

Verygood trotted happily with Cale. At the edge of the forest, where the trees stood thick, the two boys looked back. A feather of smoke curled up from the cabin chimney. The voices of Lyddy and Betsey sounded sweet and gay as they sang over their washing.

Verygood stopped and listened. "I guess I'll go back, Cale," he declared.

"Choosy chick! First thee decides to visit Father. Then thee decides to stay here."

243

Cale watched Verygood scamper homeward. He was disappointed as he entered the forest alone. All the Harveys thought the world and all of Verygood. It was because he was the baby of the family. It was because of his bright hair and bonny face. It was because he was almost always as good as his name made him out—very good.

Father was disappointed, too, when Cale arrived at the new clearing without the little boy. The day was long with nothing but the sound of their axes ringing through the woods.

It was late that Saturday afternoon when they returned to the cabin. Inside the cabin Mother straightened up from bending over the cooking kettles. She looked beyond Father and Cale. "Where's Verygood?" she asked quickly.

"Isn't he here?" All stood as still as if something had struck them. When Cale spoke at last, his voice didn't sound like his own.

"Verygood didn't go into the woods with me, Mother. He changed his mind again. I saw him run back."

"He's not been with thee the livelong day?" whispered Mother. She dropped the big stirring spoon into the kettle of mush and ran out into the clearing. "Verygood! Verygood!" she called.

244

Then they were all out, calling the little boy's name. The forest echoed with it. "Ver-ry-goo-od!"

Supper was forgotten. Betsey ran through the garden, cornfield, and barn, her eyes big and frightened. Cale and Lyddy searched the bank of South Fork. How dark and swift flowed the water under the dark branches! Father was off in the woods, calling and calling and firing his gun. Mother had become so weak she could do nothing but sit on the cabin doorstep.

Darkness fell. After a hurried bite of food Father and Cale roamed the woods again. They held the burning pine knots high, to light their way. More than once the eyes of some animal blazed from its hiding place. Cale felt that his own eyes might burst from his head as he stared into the blackness, seeking for the little brother with the bright hair.

245

The night was half gone when the weary searchers had to give up. Father's voice was rough and shaking as he read a chapter from the Bible by the light of a tallow candle. Then the Quaker family prayed silently.

The next morning Cale thought he couldn't bear it when he woke and learned that Father had gone off without him. Father had gone to seek help from other settlers. Everyone was gone but Lyddy and she had stayed at home to be with Mother.

"Father said thee is to be the man-body we need at the cabin," Lyddy explained to Cale. "He said thee is to fire thy gun three times, should any word come about Verygood."

Staying at the cabin, where it was so sorrowful and still, was the hardest thing anyone had ever asked of Cale!

The long Sunday passed. By nightfall one hundred men had gathered. Women came to bring food and comfort.

"Oh, that I had never brought my wife and children to these wild forests!" groaned Father, as he started out again on a night search with the other men.

They returned to the cabin for breakfast. As they prepared to set forth again Father said, "If Verygood is to be found alive, it must be today. So let us form a long line, never moving more than an arm's length from one another. In this way we shall comb every inch of the forest. Let us search five miles in each direction. So young a child as Verygood could not travel more than five miles."

"He who finds Verygood shall fire three shots," suggested one of the men. "If the boy is found alive, as many as know it shall fire all at once."

Eastward for five miles the line of men combed the woods. Back to the starting point, then five miles west they searched. After a short rest the start was made to the north.

The line of men was so long that some did not know, at first, of the messenger who came riding and stopped to speak to those nearest to him. But to everyone came the report of three shots. Verygood had been found! Dead or alive? Cale's heart seemed to stand still.

Suddenly there was a great firing of guns. There was a thunder of shouts. Caps flew into the air. The men laughed with joy, and shook hands.

Cale was the first to whirl and run homeward. Others followed. They were bursting with eagerness to tell the women the glad news. But the women had heard the shots. They came running to meet the men, Mother first of all.

"Where is my little son?" Mother cried.

"Alvin Johns, whose cabin stands seven miles north, will bring him home tomorrow," answered Father. "Our boy is unharmed, but he is yet too weak to travel."

How bright shone the faces in the cabin that night! There was joy in the Bible reading. The prayer was deep with thanks.

Alvin Johns came riding into the clearing next day. Their bonny little Verygood sat curled against his arm.

248

Mother reached up to take her boy. "How is thee feeling today, Mother?" asked Verygood politely. But when he saw so many eyes on him, he hid his face on her shoulder. His cheeks were scratched and mosquito-bitten. His legs hung thin. His clothes were torn and stained.

"My wife and I hadn't heard that a child was lost," Alvin Johns told them. "We thought we were seeing a ghost when the weak little lad crawled into our cabin. We fed and washed him. After he'd slept a long time, we asked him questions, and he answered, 'I guess I was a choosy chick, like Cale said, 'cause I decided to go to my father's clearing, after all. I couldn't see Cale in the woods, but I runned to catch up. I runned and runned. I was scared. I was losted.'"

"Verygood told us his name," Mr. Johns went on. "Then I knew he belonged to one of the Harvey families in this settlement. I started out and met the line of searchers. It's almost beyond belief that the boy is alive and whole."

After Mr. Johns was thanked by everyone and had left, Verygood was petted until Father said there would be no living with him. All the children hung around asking him questions, as he sat on Mother's lap.

"Didn't thee meet any wild creatures?" asked Lyddy.

Verygood looked at her, trying to remember. Suddenly he sat up, eager to tell. "Once I was sleepy. I crawled into a hollow log. D'reckly, a little black-and-white dog crep' in with me. We slept together, and I wasn't scared any more."

"A little black-and-white dog!" echoed Cale. He leaned over to sniff his small brother. Then whirling, he dashed out of doors, his hand clapped over his mouth to keep the laughter in. There was no reeky smell on Verygood but Cale was sure that the little fellow had slept with a skunk.

Cale peeped into the cabin to see if others guessed the truth and saw many eyes twinkling with laughter.

But Mother's eyes were deep and tender. "That reeky little animal knew goodness as soon as it set eyes on Verygood. It wouldn't harm a child who had no fear of it," she said softly.

Twelve-year-old Cale, who hadn't shed a tear, couldn't help crying now. It was because Mother made him see Verygood in the great dark woods —a little boy so tender and childlike that not even a skunk-creature would harm him.

Cale wiped the trickle of tears from his cheeks and suddenly all his ache and sorrow were gone. Head and hands went down. Feet went up. He turned a perfect handspring. "Yip-eee!" yelled Cale. It came out of his throat like that, shrill and happy, like heyday, like jubilee! Just like jubilee!

*Mabel Leigh Hunt*

# The Old Coach Road

There's hardly a wheel rut left to show
The way the coach road used to go.
Trees straddle it and berries grow
Where coaches rumbled long ago,
And horses' hoofs struck sparks of light,
Many a frosty winter night.
Here gypsy faces, lean and tan,
Peered from some lumbering caravan,
Or peddlers passed with bulging packs
And sheep with sun aslant their backs.
Now, only berry pickers push
Their way through thorn and elder bush—
But sometimes of a night, they say,
Wheels have been heard to pass that way.

*Rachel Lyman Field*

# The Unexpected Fawn

Everybody likes a pet to care for and love. If you looked at it one way, everybody in the Woodlawn family did have a pet. The dog belonged to everybody. Then there were always young pigs and calves and colts on the farm. But this wasn't the same as having your very own pet, and Tom and Warren wanted a pet of their own.

"Caddie has her old sheep, Nanny. And now she has Bouncer, the lamb," said Tom.

"And Hetty and Minnie each have a pet chicken," added Warren.

Caddie and Hetty and Minnie were the boys' sisters. Caddie was the oldest girl. She was nine. Tom and Warren were both older than Caddie.

"The girls have pets of their own," Warren said. "We should have a pet of our own, too."

"I know, but what?"

"Tadpoles?" asked Warren, then added thoughtfully, "Snakes, maybe."

"How many tricks could you teach a tadpole?" asked Tom. "And somehow I don't feel as if I wanted to pet a snake."

They were silent for a minute and then Tom's face brightened.

"A deer now—," he said, "that would be a pet if we could get one!"

"Yes," said Warren, "it would."

The Woodlawn family lived in the early days when much of the country was forest land. Wild animals were often seen in the woods at the edge of their farm.

In early March, when the sap started running, the boys helped their father tap the hard maple trees and hang big buckets on pegs to catch the sap. Then they often glimpsed the short white tails

of deer disappearing through the brush. But the time came for shearing of the sheep, and they still had no pet of their own.

Before the shearing started, Father came home with the news that wool was worth more if it was washed before it was sheared.

"We're going to wash all of our sheep," announced Father.

"Wash seven hundred sheep?" cried Mother. "My dear, you must have lost your wits!"

"Not at all," said Father. "I'm using my wits. We'll build large pens near the sand bar on the river. As soon as it is warm enough, we'll begin washing the sheep there. We'll turn them into the clean green pasture to dry. I can get two men from town to help the farm hands and myself and, of course, the boys can help."

"And me, Father!" cried Caddie. "Will you let me help, too?"

"Well," said Father, "we'll see how you do with Bouncer. If you can handle him, I guess you can handle anything."

"Of course I can handle Bouncer!" Caddie cried. "My very own lamb!" Bouncer had a fine coat of wool. Caddie was looking forward to the money she would get after the shearing.

The barrel of soft soap which Mother had made was taken down to the new pens near the sand bar. And on the first warm day the washing of the sheep began.

For a while Caddie stood and watched her brothers at work. Tom was hanging on to a sheep by a strap round its neck while Warren poured water and a handful of soft soap over its back and worked it into the wool.

Then they had to pull the creature into the river to wash the soap out of its wool before sending it into the pasture. This was the hardest part because the sheep hung back from going into the river.

256

It did not help a bit that someone was hunting in the woods across the river. They could hear the sound of shots and this frightened the bleating ewes and lambs all the more.

"Who ever heard of hunting in the spring!" said Warren. "That hunter had better be over here helping us wash sheep."

The shooting went on for some time but the Woodlawns soon forgot about it. The sheep needed all their attention.

Once, Father looked over at Caddie as he finished an especially lively sheep.

"You'd better change your mind, daughter. Let me wash Bouncer for you."

Caddie only shook her head. As Bouncer came from the pen, she flung the strap about his neck as she had seen the boys do, and led him across the sand bar to the edge of the river. Here he gave a sudden leap, and it was all she could do to hold him. After a moment, he stood still again and she was able to pour some water over him.

Warren helped her with the soap, and she worked it into the wool. She could see how fine and white the wool was going to be when the soap was rinsed off.

At last she said, "Come on now, Bouncer, into the river with you!"

Bouncer had other ideas about the river. He tried to run in every direction but the right one. Tom and Warren, shouting and waving him back toward the water, made him even more excited. Caddie lost the strap from his neck and could keep hold of him only by digging her fingers deep into his wool.

At last Bouncer took to the river with Caddie hanging on for dear life. But he did not return quietly to the sand bar and the pasture as the other sheep had done. He suddenly struck out into the middle of the river, swimming bravely, and Caddie swam right along with him.

258

Above the sound of the rushing water, she heard Father's voice crying out, "Hold on to him! Hold on to him! I'm coming."

The family canoe was pulled up near the sand bar. In a moment Father and the boys were in it and paddling as fast as they could, but Bouncer reached the riverbank before they did. When they came up, Caddie had flung herself awkwardly on top of her sheep and was trying hard to keep him from running off into the woods.

Father ran to get the sheep. Then he put Caddie into the canoe to paddle, and got in after her with a very quiet sheep held tightly in his arms. Bouncer seemed glad to be in the hands of someone who could get him home again! The boys pushed the canoe into the water and stood watching as it floated off. There wasn't room in it for all of them.

"I'll send one of the men back for you," Father called to them.

"Don't hurry," Warren said. "We'll go see who was shooting."

They struck into the woods beyond the river-bank, looking for signs of the hunters.

"This is a bad time of the year to hunt," said Warren. "It's the time for mothers and young things that shouldn't be killed."

"I know," said Tom. "Wonder who it was?"

They went on for a short distance without speaking until they came to a small opening under the trees. There lay a newly-killed deer.

"A doe," said Tom. "Oh, Warren, someone has shot a doe!"

Warren shook his head and stood looking down at the little body. The hunter had cut away some of the meat and left the rest to waste.

260

"A doe is sure to have a fawn hidden away somewhere at this time of year, Tom. Let's look around."

They parted and each boy went quietly through the underbrush, alert now for signs of the fawn. Tom saw it first.

Its white spots flecked on the brown were like small white blossoms on brown leaves. The fawn blended with its background so well that Tom looked at it for almost a minute before he really saw it. It was lying where its mother had left it, and keeping very still as it had learned to do.

261

Tom got down on his knees beside the little animal. His hands were slow and gentle, so that he would not frighten it. He could hear Warren crashing through the brush nearby.

He said in a quiet, warning voice, "Warren!"

"What? Did you find it, Tom? Did you find the fawn?"

"Quiet," Tom said.

"Oh, Tom!" whispered Warren, coming to stand beside him and look at the perfect little creature which lay trembling among the leaves and ferns.

Tom looked up at his brother. "Warren, he hasn't got anybody but us. Do you think we could raise him?"

"Couldn't we raise him on a bottle, like Caddie raised Bouncer?" asked Warren thoughtfully.

Tom took off his coat and gently lifted the fawn onto it. Then he picked it up in his arms.

"I guess we have our pet now, Tom," Warren said. "Do you guess so?"

"I guess so," said Tom.

They walked very softly through the woods carrying the fawn by turns, and their eyes shone with a new brightness.

*Carol Ryrie Brink*

262

# Indian Pipe and Moccasin Flower

Indian pipe and moccasin flower
   Grow where the woodland waves,
Grow in the moss and the bracken bower
   Trod by the light-foot braves
Who played their part, who lived their hour
   And left, with a name that thrills,
Indian pipe and moccasin flower
   Scattered among our hills.

*Arthur Guiterman*

263

# Riding the Pony Express

Sally Mason was baking cinnamon rolls on a summer morning in 1861. Her brother, Randy, would like something to eat when he rode in late that afternoon to change horses. It would be his last lap before he turned the mail over to the next Pony Express rider at Placerville.

Randy would stop only long enough to toss the saddle and its heavy sacks of mail from the tired horse to a fresh one. Then he would be off again. Mrs. Mason always had a cup of hot coffee ready for him, with cake or rolls to be taken along. This morning she was caring for a sick neighbor and twelve-year-old Sally was taking her place.

Sally pulled the pan of cinnamon rolls out of the oven just as a shadow appeared in the doorway. It was Old Suzy, an Indian woman, as broad as she was high. She was carrying an empty basket.

"Oh, Suzy!" cried Sally. "You're going for berries. I'll get a pail and go with you. There's time enough before Randy comes."

Sally put two of the hot rolls in the Indian woman's basket. Old Suzy's face crinkled up

until her beady black eyes disappeared. Her face
was burned almost black by years of mountain sun
and wind.

Old Suzy and Sally climbed the hill behind the
stable. The wind was blowing in fitful gusts.
Sally was puffing, but Old Suzy climbed steadily
upward. They stopped at a high meadow.

Suzy's basket was nearly full and Sally's pail
half full, when Old Suzy straightened her back
and pointed.

"Rain come," she said, and started down.

265

Sally followed. Old Suzy turned off below the meadow. In a clearing by a stream there was a tumble-down log cabin. As they reached it, big drops of rain began to splash on the shaky roof. In a few seconds the downpour was deafening, and Old Suzy shut the sagging door against it. It was dark in the cabin with only a little light that came through the cracks between the logs.

Old Suzy stood by the door looking through one of these cracks. Suddenly she caught Sally's arm and pulled her down into a corner. At the same time she dragged an old packing box and a broken chair to put in front of them.

"Black Jack come," grunted Old Suzy. "Him bad." Sally heard voices, and two men pushed open the door of the cabin.

"Lucky you knew this was here!" said the smaller of the men.

"Pays to know good hideouts in these parts," answered the man, who Sally knew was Black Jack, the heartless outlaw.

"This is as good a place as any to talk," said Black Jack, as the two men stood in the doorway. "Randy Mason comes through here around four. I hear he's carrying a lot of money this trip. I plan to stop him at Arch Rock."

"But that's U.S. mail!" said the other man.

"It's the money I'm after," said Black Jack. "If he hands that over, he can have the mail. If he doesn't . . ." Black Jack shrugged.

"I don't like it," the smaller man whined.

"It's easy money," said Black Jack. "There's just one chance. That's why you're in on this. Since this rain came, Randy may take the cutoff back of his place. He might figure that the ford's high. If he does, he'll come out just below the Gap. You wait there. If you're afraid to shoot, hold him until I come. I may have trouble getting through the ford myself."

"It's risky," the other man protested.

"So's pannin' gold. So's everything. Stop whining and come on. The rain's lettin' up. You can cache your share of the money here in this cabin till the excitement blows over."

267

After the two men had gone, Old Suzy held
Sally back for several minutes. Then she let her
go and Sally plunged down the hill, forgetting
her pail of berries. She built up the fire with
trembling hands. She put on the coffee and slid
the pan of rolls into the warm oven. It seemed
no time before she heard the wild coyote yell
Randy always gave as he came down the trail.

Sally met him at the corral. While he pulled
his saddle and blanket from the heaving back of
the pony and tossed it onto his fresh horse, Sally
poured out her story.

268

Randy stuffed the rolls into a leather pouch slung over his deerskin shirt, and gulped down the hot coffee.

"Good kid!" he said, with a grin. "I'll take the cutoff. I meant to anyway after this storm. I'd rather face the other man on the upper trail than that bandit, Black Jack, at Arch Rock. Now listen, Sally."

Sally put out a protesting hand, but he shook her off. "Listen carefully," he said. "The Express money is sewn into the saddle lining. The pouches that usually carry the mail are stuffed with old envelopes and papers. The regular mail is rolled in my saddle blanket. I'll throw him the pouches and I may get through."

Randy handed Sally the empty mug. "You can see the Gap from here, Sal. Usually I make it in twenty minutes. The mud will slow me down. Give me thirty minutes. Saddle your horse as soon as I leave. Then come out here where you can see clearly. If you don't see me wave my hat at you as I ride through that Gap thirty minutes from now, take the cutoff and find out why."

He turned his horse, jumped into the saddle, and was gone down the trail in a splash of mud.

269

"So long," he yelled, waving his hat as his pony plunged into the trees.

Sally saddled her horse. She changed her cotton print dress for a pair of Randy's buckskins and a leather shirt. She covered her braids with one of his hats. She kept careful track of the time.

When there were just five minutes to go, she walked her horse out to the gate where she had a clear view of the Gap. In her hand was her father's little minute glass. She watched the Gap, keeping half an eye on the sifting sand. Five times she turned the little glass and watched the sand sift to the bottom. Then she jumped quickly on her horse and started up the cutoff trail.

She found Randy on the main trail below the Gap. The short man she had seen at the cabin lay in a puddle of mud. Randy's horse was dead. Randy lay on the ground beside his horse, frantically trying to get the saddle blanket untied.

"Oh, Sal!" he cried in relief. "You're in time. Get this blanket off and onto your horse. Never mind anything else. We can't get the saddle off. The horse is lying on it. Ride for all you're worth into Placerville. Turn the mail over to Rogers at the station."

270

"You're hurt!" said Sally. "I can't leave you here in this mud."

"You're to do as I say," Randy ordered. "Change this blanket over. Get going."

A figure glided out of the woods. Sally thought it was Black Jack and her heart jumped.

"Old Suzy!" cried Randy. "Good Old Suzy!"

"How did you know where to come?" asked Sally.

271

"Suzy hear." The Indian woman stooped and lifted Randy like a sack of meal across her shoulder. She carried him into the woods. When she came back she had Randy's gun belt strapped about her broad waist. She stripped the saddle off Sally's horse. Then she heaved the dead horse off the stirrup and tugged until she had freed Randy's saddle. She and Sally put that saddle on Sally's horse. They tied the blanket behind it. Sally worked frantically. She expected Black Jack to come down the trail any moment.

"Black Jack come by and by," said Old Suzy.

"What's keeping him?" asked Sally.

Old Suzy shrugged. "Horse gone," she said. "He tie horse by tree. He go sit Arch Rock. Suzy cut rein with sharp rock. Give him horse big slap." Her beady black eyes were lost in a mass of crinkles.

Sally swung herself into the saddle. "Good Old Suzy!" she said.

Suzy grunted. Sally dug her heels in her horse's flanks and started up the steep grade to the Gap.

Two hours later, after a hard ride, she galloped into the mining town of Placerville and up to the Pony Express station.

272

"Thought you'd never get here," shouted the angry voice of Rogers, the waiting rider. "You're an hour late." And then, "Why, you're not Randy. You're a girl. Who're you?"

"I'm Sally, Randy Mason's sister," said Sally, sliding out of the saddle. "There was a hold-up. Randy's hurt and can't ride. The money's sewn inside the saddle, and the mail is in the blanket." Sally felt slightly dizzy and her knees were trembling. She could hardly stand.

With a practiced hand, the rider slid the saddle onto his fresh horse. He fastened the blanket behind his saddle, leaped upon the horse, and whirled away in a clatter of hoofs.

He waved. "You did all right for a girl!" he shouted back to her. "Ridin' for the Pony Express."

*Marion Garthwaite*

273

# The Railroad Cars Are Coming

The great Pacific railway,
  For California hail!
Bring on the locomotive,
  Lay down the iron rail;
Across the rolling prairies
  By steam we're bound to go.
The railroad cars are coming, humming
  Through New Mexico.

The little dogs in dog-town
  Will wag each little tail;
They'll think that something's coming
  A'riding on a rail.
The rattlesnake will show its fangs,
  The owl tu-whit, tu-who,
The railroad cars are coming, humming
  Through New Mexico,
The railroad cars are coming, humming
  Through New Mexico.

*Carl Sandburg*

274

# The Grizzly

Pa got into the wagon and picked up the reins. The burros swung their long ears forward, awaiting the signal to start. But Pa didn't give the signal, not right away. Instead he turned to Mikey, who was standing beside the wagon.

"Remember what I told you," he said. "I'm leaving you in charge. Be sure to keep the gun loaded—you know where the bullets are. Keep your eye on the little ones, and don't let them wander off into the forest. They might meet that grizzly."

"Yes sir, Pa," Mikey promised. "I'll keep my eye on things."

He straightened his shoulders and some of the unhappiness left his face. Mikey had especially wanted to go on this trip to the city with his father and two older brothers. He had not been out of these mountains since he and his family had come to live here many months ago. He had felt that he was big enough to follow beside the load of tanbark to the city at the foot of the long range of mountains, the city beside the sea. But father had said, "No."

Then last night a stranger had come to their home among the redwoods. He had stayed with them overnight and told an exciting tale of a great grizzly bear which had been shot at but had escaped into the forest.

"Better be on the watch for him," the stranger said. "He might have been hit, and a wounded animal is very dangerous."

So now Pa was warning Mikey about the bear and about taking care of the little ones. Maybe Pa had planned for him to stay behind to guard the family! Now that he was ten years old, he was big enough for the responsibility. Anyway that's what Mikey thought.

276

"Let's go, Pat," Pa called to his oldest son who was waiting in front of the team.

Pat started down the path. Pa said, "Giddap," and slowly the little burros started forward. All summer Pa and the boys had worked peeling tanbark off the tanbark oaks. Now the time had come to take the strips of bark to the tannery in the city.

Next morning when Mikey woke up he could hear his mother and sister moving around in the lean-to kitchen of their log house. He felt warm and comfortable in bed under the quilts until he remembered that Pa had left him to be the man of the house. Then he jumped quickly out onto the cold floor. The mist drifting in from the window made him shiver.

After breakfast, Mikey took the ax and the gun and set off to cut firewood. He would have to cut plenty to be ready for the rainy weather which would begin in a few weeks. The first trees Pa had chopped down were dry enough to cut. Mikey went to work. He could feel his muscles bulge when he chopped the tough wood.

All that day he chopped wood, and by supper-time he had quite a pile of it. After Pa came back, they would haul the wood to the house.

By the time Mikey had finished milking on the second day, the sky was dark with mist. But by the time the cows were put in their stalls, the mist had become lighter. The moon was up.

He made sure the chickens were all in and listened for a moment to the peaceful clucking of the hens before fastening the door of the cowshed for the night. Then picking up the two pails of milk, Mikey started toward the house.

Suddenly his heart stood still! He stared in horror at a black hulk shuffling toward him out of the forest. He couldn't make out its shape, but he knew what it was. Only a grizzly could look as big as that.

He didn't have a gun. What could he do?

Without waiting to think, he raced for the kitchen door. The milk splashed out of the pails as he kicked it open.

278

Ma looked at him in astonishment as he stumbled in. "What . . ." she began.

"The grizzly," Mikey gasped. He bolted the door, and stood inside trembling from his fright.

Ma went calmly through the rooms to see that all the shutters were bolted tightly, and big sister Martha checked the bolts on the other two doors.

Ma put the little ones into their trundle bed, but they were too frightened to go to sleep. Finally Ma sat beside the bed and sang to them until their tired eyes dropped shut.

Mikey was glad he had shut up the cows before the bear came. If he hadn't, there might not be any cows by morning. He walked slowly through

the rooms, listening to the bear sniff around the house. He wondered if the shutters would hold if the bear really tried to get inside. The grizzly spent most of his time sniffing around the outside of the kitchen. He seemed to smell the food.

Martha and Ma went about their kitchen work as if the sniffing came from a deer. But Mikey knew they were frightened too. How long would the bear stay? Would he keep them in the house for the next five or six days until Pa came back? Mikey knew the cows would have to be fed and milked and watered before then.

Mikey went up the ladder to the loft. He peered out the window through the mist, bright with moonlight. Below him was the bear. He shuddered at the sight of that huge black hulk. He had never dreamed that grizzlies were so big!

But seeing the bear below gave him an idea. He went downstairs, took the gun down from the pegs on the wall, and got the extra bullets. Up in the loft again, he made sure the gun was ready to shoot, and then put the extra bullets into his pocket. He looked out the window, but the bear had gone around the corner of the house.

Mikey thought of a daring plan. If it worked, fine. If it didn't—well, he just wouldn't think of that. Pa had left him in charge. He wasn't going to let that bear hurt Ma or Martha or the little ones.

He stood up in the loft window, facing the house, and looked across the roof. He had climbed onto the roof once before this way. He was sure he could do it again. Carefully, he placed the gun on the roof so it wouldn't slide away. Then he pulled himself carefully over the edge of the eaves and drew his legs up. Safe on top, he stopped a minute to catch his breath. He was outside with the bear now, and he hoped the bear wasn't tall enough to climb onto the roof of the lean-to.

Quietly he crept down the slope of the roof to the edge. He'd have to be close when he shot the bear. He could hear it sniffing along the kitchen wall, raking the boards with its claws and shaking the shutters, as it shuffled along.

Mikey stretched out on his stomach and readied the gun toward the place where he could hear the bear. He was almost on the edge of the roof, but he didn't dare lean over. When he was ready, he took a deep breath. He took another deep breath. Why didn't the bear hear his heart pounding and look up?

He whistled sharply.

The bear rose to his hind feet to see where the noise came from. Mikey shot.

With a roar, the bear crashed against the house. Mikey trembled as he reloaded the gun in the dim light. The bear had been so tall, standing on its hind legs, that it could have reached out and cuffed him!

282

He got to his knees and looked carefully over the edge of the roof. The bear was trying to rise. Mikey aimed again and fired. The bear quivered and lay still. Mikey wasn't taking any chances. He fired twice more.

He could hear Ma and Martha running across the loft to the window.

"Mikey, Mikey!" Ma called. "Are you all right?"

Mikey watched the bear for a few minutes to be sure it was dead. Then he walked up the roof to the ridge. "I'm all right, Ma," he said softly. "Here, take the gun." He held it over the edge of the eaves and Ma took it. Then he lowered himself to the window ledge, feet first, and Ma and Martha helped him through the window.

He staggered to his bed and flopped down on it, worn out.

"Oh Ma, I was never so scared in my life! The bear was big as—as—as a redwood tree!" Mikey stammered. He buried his face in his hands and sobbed.

Ma patted him on the shoulder. "There, there, Mikey. Every brave person is afraid. A person is brave because he does what he should, even when he is scared."

283

Mikey blinked back the tears and looked up at her. "Do you really mean that, Ma?"

"That's right, Mikey. If a man isn't afraid, he really isn't being brave at all. Come down to the kitchen and have a hot drink," Ma said softly. "You're cold."

Mikey felt better now and followed her willingly down to the warm kitchen. She heated some milk at the fireplace in the front room. Martha put it into Pa's coffee mug with a big chunk of butter that soon melted into golden bubbles. Mikey sat on a stool at the kitchen table sipping it.

Mikey finished the hot milk and said good-night. He climbed into his bed in the loft and was soon sound asleep.

The rooster was crowing the next morning when Mikey ran quietly down the ladder and outside into the mist to take a close look at the bear. In the dim light it looked like a huge black rock against the house. Mikey was proud that he had been able to save the family. He could hardly wait for Pa to come home. Pa had left him to be the man of the house. Here was the dead grizzly to prove that he had been worthy of the trust.

*Betty Stirling*

# The Flower-Fed Buffaloes

The flower-fed buffaloes of the spring
In the days of long ago,
Ranged where the locomotives sing
And the prairie flowers lie low:—
The tossing, blooming, perfumed grass
Is swept away by the wheat,
Wheels and wheels and wheels spin by
In the spring that still is sweet.
But the flower-fed buffaloes of the spring
Left us long ago.
They gore no more, they bellow no more,
They trundle around the hills no more:—
With the Blackfeet, lying low,
With the Pawnees, lying low,
Lying low.

*Vachel Lindsay*

285

# Courage Leads the Way

Once upon a time there was a princess. In this way do most of our favorite fairy tales begin. But this story is not a fairy tale. The "once upon a time" was when our country was very young, and the princess was an Indian girl. She was a Shoshone princess. Her name was Sacajawea.

In 1803 the United States bought from France a great tract of land west of the Mississippi River. Few white men had ever gone into it.

The American people wanted to know more about the land they had bought. They wanted to know about the plant and animal life, and what minerals could be found there. They were interested in the Indians and how they lived.

Two young men were chosen to lead an exploring party of about thirty men. They were to explore the river valleys and plains and find a way across the mountains to the Pacific Ocean.

286

The two young leaders were Meriwether Lewis and William Clark. They and their men started up the Missouri River in the spring of 1804. They traveled over a thousand miles. Then one day they beached their boats on the riverbank where an Indian village stood.

The white men built a strong fort and inside it they built log cabins. They had decided to spend the winter months here on the banks of the Missouri. When spring came, the ice and snow would be gone. Then they could set forth again upon their journey into the unknown West. They called their winter home Fort Mandan.

287

It happened that the village where they stopped was the one in which Sacajawea lived. She was the wife of Charbonneau, a Frenchman, who traded among the Indians and made his home in this village with the Mandan tribe.

Sacajawea's own people, the Shoshones, lived far to the west in the Snake River country and she dreamed of returning to them. She longed to see her family. When she was a little girl, an enemy tribe had taken her captive and carried her down the long rivers toward the east.

On a windy day in April, 1805, Charbonneau said to his young wife, "Come with me."

Sacajawea knew better than to ask why. Indian wives did not question their husbands. She picked up her baby and quietly followed Charbonneau.

Spring had come to the prairies. Birds were migrating to their summer homes. The green grass gave promise of good grazing for the herds of buffalo upon which the Indians depended for their food. The willows by the river showed a tender green along their branches. The river itself flowed swiftly, fed by melting snow.

To Sacajawea's surprise, her husband led her straight to the fort where Meriwether Lewis and William Clark were waiting.

288

"Sacajawea!" Captain Lewis spoke her name. "We have lately learned that you belong to the tribe of the Shoshones far to the west."

Sacajawea bowed her head, too shy to speak. Captain Lewis continued, "We are leaving in a few days for the western lands. We want you to guide us to the lands of your people. Charbonneau, your husband, will go along with us as our chief cook. Will you come?"

Shyly Sacajawea glanced at her husband. It was for him to say. But her eyes were shining with eagerness.

"She will do it," declared Charbonneau. "She will take you as far as you wish to go, and she will bring you back again."

So one day shortly after her visit to the white man's fort, Sacajawea started out as a guide for the party that was to explore the unknown West.

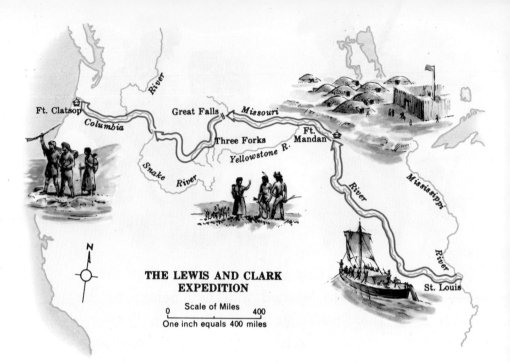

THE LEWIS AND CLARK
EXPEDITION

Scale of Miles
0          400
One inch equals 400 miles

During the rest of April and on into May, as they traveled west on the Missouri, their only serious threat of danger came from the fierce grizzly bears. They would attack the scouting parties who left the safety of the dugout canoes to explore this new land and to hunt for food for the party. There were several narrow escapes.

Then one day in May they faced danger of another kind. Only the cool head of the Indian princess saved them. The men had fastened a sail to one of the dugouts in order to speed it through the water. Sacajawea was in this boat and her husband was at the tiller, steering.

Suddenly a heavy wind arose and the gusts hit the sail with such force that the boat tipped over on its side. But for the sail, which now lay close above the water, the canoe would certainly have gone under.

The contents of the boat were spilled out into the racing river, and it looked as if the people would be thrown out too. The current was too swift for swimming. Anyone who fell into it would drown before he could be pulled out. The other men in the boat realized this and struggled to do what they could to right it.

But Charbonneau, seeing the danger, was so paralyzed with fear that he let go of the tiller. This left the dugout helpless in the fierce wind.

"Help me! Save me!" screamed Charbonneau.

It was a lucky thing for the explorers that his wife was no coward. Sacajawea saw neither swift water nor danger. She saw only that some of the precious things belonging to the Captains were about to be lost forever.

She did not think of her own safety, as she tried to rescue the maps and reports which had been spilled into the water. She reached far out, scooped up the floating papers, and dumped them back into the madly gliding boat.

Again and again she reached. Each time her hand caught more of the papers, until she had saved them all. The exploring party would have been helpless without its maps, for they showed the general direction of rivers and where the mountains lay. Without them even Sacajawea could not have guided the party over the long trail to the Pacific coast.

The dugout was finally brought under control when one of the men lost his temper and threatened to shoot Charbonneau if he did not grasp the tiller. The cowardly trader, more afraid of the gun than the water, did as he was ordered, and everything was saved.

Captain Lewis
was very grateful
to Sacajawea for her
bravery and quick thinking.
To reward her, he named
one of the rivers the Sacajawea.
Many times later the Indian girl's knowledge of
the wilderness and her patience and good temper
saved the lives of the white men and made their
journey easier.

It was late July when they reached the place
where three rivers joined to form the Missouri.
Sacajawea knew this to be near where she had
been captured as a child. She was happy for she
knew that the Shoshones generally crossed the
mountains to hunt along these rivers. There was
a chance that they might meet some of her people.

They did meet a party of Shoshone hunters.
Their chief was with them and when he came
forward to greet the white men, Sacajawea found
herself looking into the proud face of her brother.

The Indian princess had returned. The news
reached the village ahead of the party, and the
Shoshones rushed out to greet her. These were
her people. These were the ones she had come
so far to see. She was overjoyed. Her dream
had come true.

Now the white men knew that whatever the
expedition needed in the way of food and horses
for the long, hard journey to the Pacific coast
would be given them. They were not disappointed.
The Shoshones gave generous gifts to these men
who were friends of Sacajawea, sister of their
chief.

It was November when Sacajawea finally stood
on the shores of the "Big Water." That was her

name for the Pacific Ocean. Her eyes were big with wonder as she gazed upon water that reached in front of her as far as she could see.

What a tale she would have to tell in that Mandan village to which she would soon return with her husband and her little son! For now that the Pacific had been reached and the farthest western lands had been explored, the white men would be turning back. They would take the report of their travels to the people of America.

As on their setting forth, the Indian Sacajawea would lead them on the return journey. Back over the mountains, across the prairies, through danger and hardship, she would show them the way home. In the face of danger she would again be steadfast and unafraid and faithful to their need of her.

And some day, a hundred years later, a great and grateful nation would remember the part she had played in its history. Its people would speak her name with honor and with pride. No story of the United States would be complete which did not mention the name of Sacajawea, the gentle Indian princess who led Lewis and Clark along the trail to the sunset.

*Doris Gates*

# Cottonwood Leaves

Red firelight on the Sioux tepees,
   (Oh, the camp-smoke down the wind!)
Red firelight on the cottonwood trees
That clap, clap, clap in the dry night breeze.
   (Oh, the camp-smoke down the wind!)

Red-skinned braves in the circling dance;
   (Oh, the bright sparks toward the stars!)
The moccasined feet that stamp and prance
And the brandished knife and the lifted lance.
   (Oh, the bright sparks toward the stars!)

Eagle plumes in the swirling troop,
   (Oh, the wild flame leaping high!)
And the painted bodies ramp and stoop
To the drum's hot thump and the vaunting whoop.
   (Oh, the wild flame leaping high!)

296

Back where the darkness drops its veil
    (Oh, the sad smoke drifting low!)
The far wolves howl and the widows wail
For the graveless dead on the grim war trail.
    (Oh, the sad smoke drifting low!)

Night on the plains, and the dreams it weaves,
    (Oh, the embers black and cold!)
Where painted ghosts with the step of thieves
Dance to the clap of the cottonwood leaves.
    (Oh, the embers black and cold!)

*Badger Clark*

# Things to Think About and Do

1. If there had been modern signs along the trail, pioneers might have read signs like these below. Match each sign with a story in this unit. In what state or states might each sign be found?

Welcome to Placerville      Slow! Sheep Crossing
10 Mi. to Columbia Gorge    Tanbark Sold Here
Quaker Meetinghouse      Shoshone Ponies for Sale
     See the World's Largest Bearskin Rug

2. Write a pioneer story full of modern things. Read it to your class and see how many of your tricks are noticed. Ask your classmates to tell how they know each modern thing could not be true.

3. Tell what the following expressions meant in pioneer times.

     up the ladder to the loft      the ford's high
     burning pine knots      in this settlement
     my father's clearing      little minute glass
     a barrel of soft soap      the dugout canoe

4. What would be done today

     to find a lost child?
     to prevent a robbery of the U.S. mail?
     to catch a hunter who had broken the law?
     to trap a wounded grizzly?
     to explore a new tract of land?

5. The words below describe feelings the reader might have when reading "Lost Boy." Copy and underline the words that tell how you felt.

| | | | |
|---|---|---|---|
| satisfied | worried | anxious | puzzled |
| relieved | excited | pleased | disappointed |
| pity | bored | queer | understanding |

6. Write four supporting details under this main idea from "The Unexpected Fawn."

Everybody in the Woodlawn family had a pet.

7. Prepare questions and answers to use in an interview with a pony express rider about his job. Ask a friend to help you give your interview.

8. Make a chart to show how the grizzly is different in height, weight, and fierceness from other bears. Exhibit the books you used and your chart in your classroom library.

9. Suggest other titles for "Courage Leads the Way." Explain each suggestion. Would "Rivers Lead the Way" be a good title? Why?

10. Pretend that you were in the army and went with Lewis and Clark on their expedition. Your own small pack of things could weigh no more than two and one-half pounds. What did you take? Explain your choices.

# Some Books to Read

*The Cabin Faced West*, by Jean Fritz.

When General Washington stays for supper at their cabin in western Pennsylvania and expresses his faith in this western country, Abigail is no longer homesick for Gettysburg.

*Children of the Covered Wagon*, by Mary Jane Carr.

On a hard and dangerous journey from Missouri to Oregon in 1814, these children showed great courage.

*Daniel Boone*, by John Mason Brown.

The author draws a lively picture of Daniel Boone as a hunter, pioneer, and leader.

*Down the Mississippi*, by Clyde Robert Bulla.

A farm boy has exciting adventures on the great river during pioneer times.

*Fence across the Trail*, by Elsa Falk.

A pioneer girl, with the help of Indians, rescues her brother's runaway horse.

*Tree in the Trail*, by Holling C. Holling.

A cottonwood looks down on generations of men who pass beneath its branches as they travel the Santa Fe Trail.

*Tomorrow Will Be Bright*, by Mabel Leigh Hunt.

A Quaker girl and her brother find adventure as they move westward on the long trail from North Carolina to Ohio.

Great
Old Tales

# Pandora

The old, old storytellers say that once there lived a youth named Epimetheus. He was loved by all the gods because he was good and fair to look upon. He lived all by himself in a pleasant dwelling. All day birds sang around his house, and all through the year bright flowers bloomed in his garden. No cold winds ever blew upon it, and the sun never beat down too strongly.

Epimetheus had all that his heart could wish. For this was in the time when the world was young.

Imagine, if you can, a world free of trouble. Nobody sick, nobody poor, nobody unhappy! Then trouble came into the world, and this is how it happened.

The gods, who watched over Epimetheus and took pleasure in his happiness, decided to make him a gift. They decided to give him a friend to live in his house and to share the sunshine, the songs of birds, and the perfume of flowers.

"A friend is good," the gods said to each other. "It is not good for a man to live alone."

So they made another human being and called her Pandora. They made her smaller than

Epimetheus, so that he would always be master in his house. But they made her even more beautiful than he. They gave her laughing blue eyes and golden hair. They gave her gifts of grace and goodness. They made her gentle, kind, and generous. And then just before she was to go down to earth and share with Epimetheus his pleasant dwelling, the gods made her one last gift. They gave her curiosity.

Epimetheus was delighted with his beautiful companion. They roamed the fields together. And so gentle was Pandora that the birds came to light upon her shoulders and to rub their heads against her cheeks. She would laugh gaily and stroke their feathers.

Epimetheus, watching Pandora, would think how dull his days had been before she came to brighten them.

Now one day an old man arrived at the house of Epimetheus. He was stooping under the weight of a large box which he carried on his back. Epimetheus begged him to stay and rest a while before continuing on his travels. The old man set down the box as if it were heavy enough to hold all the trouble in the world (if there had been any trouble in those days).

Then he said he must go on his way, but that he should like to leave the heavy box behind and get it again when he returned that way.

To this plan the youthful Epimetheus readily agreed, for he was goodhearted and eager to help the old man with his burden. Never would he have guessed from his looks that this old traveler was really one of the gods in disguise.

Just then Pandora came running in from the garden. When she saw the beautifully decorated box, she cried out with pleasure and fell to her knees before it. Certainly it was no ordinary box. Its sides were covered with strange carvings, and around it was a golden cord tied into a strange knot. Epimetheus too bent over to see it better. But when he straightened up to ask the stranger some question about it, the old man had gone.

Pandora and Epimetheus hunted him throughout the garden and up the road and across the meadow, but he was nowhere to be found. One moment he was there beside them, and the next moment he was gone. Then they knew he was not an ordinary person. They wondered if he might be some god, and why he had stopped at their dwelling. They asked each other what the box might hold.

"Well, whatever is in it is none of our business," said Epimetheus at last to Pandora. "Come and play as we used to do. Forget about the box."

But Pandora had been given the gift of curiosity. The more Epimetheus urged her to stay away from the box, the stronger became her desire to know what was in it. Wherever she went, whatever she did, the box was forever in her mind.

At last the desire to open it was so great that she was no longer happy. She was so curious about what the box contained that she did nothing but sit in front of it hour after hour.

One day when Epimetheus had left her sitting in front of the box, Pandora decided to untie the golden cord. Though the knot was a strange one, it did not look difficult, and she longed to see if she could undo it. She knelt down and in a twinkling was at work upon the knot. In no time the golden cord fell away. Now all Pandora had to do was to lift up the lid and peep inside. Then she could fasten the cord again, and Epimetheus would never know what she had done.

For a long moment she sat thinking. She knew she should not lift the lid, but still her curiosity drove her on to do it.

Just at that moment, she heard little voices coming out of the box. "Lift up the lid, Pandora. Lift up the lid and let us out."

For a moment Pandora was startled. Then a new curiosity took hold of her. Now she must know who was calling to her. And, besides, the poor little creatures didn't want to be shut up in an old box.

306

"Lift up the lid, Pandora," they cried again. "Let us out!"

So Pandora put her hands on the lid of the box and started to lift it. But no sooner had she opened it the tiniest crack than out rushed a swarm of ugly little creatures no bigger than insects. They flew at her and stung her wherever they could touch her.

Poor Pandora cried out and ran from the room to find Epimetheus. But the horrid creatures flew after her. And when she found Epimetheus, they flew at him too, and soon both of them were covered with stings, like insect bites.

"Oh, Pandora," cried Epimetheus, "what have you done?"

"I opened the box just a very little, and all these ugly, horrid things came rushing out," she cried.

Just how much trouble her curiosity had caused them, they did not know until later. For these evil little creatures were all the many troubles that are to be found in the world today. Sickness, cruelty, grief, want, and fear—all came flying into the world when Pandora opened the box, so the old, old storytellers say.

When at last the swarm had flown out into the garden to settle on the flowers and the grass, Pandora thought of the box once more. She was eager now to see what else it might contain. Surely the worst that it could hold had already left it! She was still curious to know what might yet remain within it.

She returned to the box and knelt down once more before it.

This time she heard a very soft and gentle voice say, "Open the box, Pandora, and let me out. Please, Pandora, open the box."

Epimetheus, who had by this time joined Pandora, begged her not to do it. "Who knows what further trouble you may set loose in the world?" he said.

308

But Pandora thought that no one with so gentle and sweet a voice could wish to cause anyone trouble. Again the voice called softly to her, "Open the box, Pandora. Do not be afraid."

So Pandora opened the box, and out flew a dainty fairylike creature. Straight at Pandora she flew, then at Epimetheus, and touched their smarting flesh with her soft wings. No sooner had she done so than all their pain left them, and they were as they had been before Pandora had first opened the box.

"Who are you?" asked Pandora, drying her tears and smiling again.

"I am Hope," replied the dainty creature. "As long as I am in the world, your troubles will never be too great for you to bear."

And so, while Pandora's curiosity filled the world with trouble, it also gave us hope. As long as we have hope, troubles can never completely get the better of us.

Anyway, that's how it all happened according to the old, old storytellers who first told the story when the world was young.

*A Greek Myth*

# A Horse Afraid of His Shadow

One day long, long ago in the ancient land of Macedonia the horse market was crowded with buyers. King Philip II himself was there. With him were the keepers of his royal stables. A fine lot of horses had been gathered for selling. First to choose would be the king and his warriors.

At the side of King Philip stood his young son, Alexander, a boy then twelve years of age. None in that crowd of buyers had a better eye for a good horse than this lad. No boys of his age in all Macedonia could compare with the young Alexander in horsemanship.

"Look well at all the animals, my son," King Philip said. "Then tell me which one you would choose from among them."

310

"Many of these colts are fine animals, my father," the boy replied. "Many have spirit. They would go bravely to battle. But none is so noble as the young black stallion yonder, that one with the white mark shaped like an ox's head on his face."

"The young prince chooses well," the black stallion's owner cried. "That is the finest colt in all the market today. My price for him is high, but I will be honest with you. That young black stallion will wear a saddle and bridle, but he will not be ridden. He is wild as the North Wind. None can stay long upon his back." The black colt even then was prancing and snorting as the noisy crowd gathered around him.

"No other horse here can compare with that one," Alexander repeated. "Surely skilled horsemen from the palace stables can tame him."

"Let the black stallion be ridden!" King Philip ordered.

The most daring horsemen of his court mounted the colt, but the trader had spoken truly. One after another they were thrown from his back when they tried to ride him over the plain.

The colt started at every sound. As soon as one tried to ride him away, he pranced, whirled, and reared high. He gave one powerful twist, and his rider was gone from his back.

"Are you satisfied now, my son, that this horse is not worth the buying?" the king asked Alexander.

"No, Father, I still say the black stallion is the very best in this market place. His riders do not understand him. He does not trust them. Let me try my hand on his bridle."

The king was pleased with his son's courage. He had no fear for his safety. The boy knew how to fall off a horse as well as how to ride one.

"Ride him then, Alexander!" the king said. "If you are successful where others have failed, I will buy the horse for you."

312

The men in the horse market were surprised to see the fearless lad leap into the saddle. Instead of rearing up, the spirited black horse stood still. Alexander talked to him softly and stroked his neck with gentle hands, then turned his head straight toward the afternoon sun and galloped away over the plain.

It grew late. The sun was setting when the anxious crowd saw the boy coming back. Swift as an arrow in flight the black stallion was galloping, galloping, but the boy was still on his back. Easily Alexander reined in the spirited stallion, which now seemed tame as a kitten.

313

"Well ridden, my son! The black stallion is yours," King Philip cried.

"Tell us your secret, young prince," the palace horsemen cried. "How did you tame that wild spirit so easily?"

"It was as I said," Alexander replied. "You did not understand him. This stallion is a horse of high and noble spirit. He starts at the sight of each moving thing that is strange to him. While the others were trying to ride him, I saw that what frightened him the most was his own moving shadow. When he ran from the sun, the black shadow leaped along, just under his nose. I took care to turn his face toward the sun, so that his shadow could not be seen. The horse forgot his fear. I let him gallop to his heart's content, and now he trusts me as his master."

The king was so proud of his son's horsemanship and his courage that he was weeping as he said, "One day you will make a great king, Alexander, but you must conquer and rule over larger kingdoms. The one I shall leave for you will be too small for your powers."

When Alexander was twenty years old, he came to the throne of Macedonia. He was called Alexander the Great, for many were the lands

into which he led his warriors, and many were the deeds for which he was famous.

The shining black stallion was Alexander's companion in battle throughout its life. He lived to be thirty years old, but at last, in a battle to conquer all India, the brave horse was sorely wounded. Straightway he galloped out of the battle. He carried his master to a safe place before he fell to the ground. On that spot by a river, Alexander the Great built a city in honor of his beloved stallion.

*Frances Carpenter*

# The Boy and the Wolf

A boy employed to guard the sheep
Despised his work. He liked to sleep.
And when a lamb was lost, he'd shout,
"Wolf! Wolf! The wolves are all about!"

The neighbors searched from noon till nine,
But of the beast there was no sign.
Yet "Wolf!" he cried next morning when
The villagers came out again.

One evening around six o'clock
A real wolf fell upon the flock.
"Wolf!" yelled the boy. "A wolf indeed!"
But no one paid him any heed.

Although he screamed to wake the dead,
"He's fooled us every time," they said,
And let the hungry wolf enjoy
His feast of mutton, lamb—and boy.

The Moral's this: The man who's wise
Does not defend himself with lies.
Liars are not believed, forsooth,
Even when liars tell the truth.

*Louis Untermeyer (From the Greek of Aesop)*

## Androcles and the Lion

Once long ago in the city of Rome there was a slave named Androcles. He served his master well, but was rewarded with cruel treatment.

At last a chance came to make his escape, and Androcles fled to the forest. Alone and frightened, he wandered about seeking a safe place to hide.

One day in his wanderings Androcles came upon a lion. His first thought was to get away before the beast pounced upon him. Then he noticed that the lion seemed to be in pain, moaning and whimpering pitifully and holding out his paw.

Slowly the slave came near enough to see that the paw was swollen and bleeding. A long sharp thorn had worked its way under the skin and was causing great pain. Androcles held the paw gently, gave a quick pull, and out came the thorn.

The lion licked the man's hand like a dog to show that he was grateful, and Androcles was no longer afraid. He followed the lion to his lair where the two lay down together and slept side by side. Here the slave could hide safely from his cruel master and the lion could wait for his wound to heal.

When at last the deep wound had healed, the lion was ready to go hunting again. Every day he went deep into the forest and returned with fresh meat for Androcles.

After a time Androcles began to roam the forest, sometimes with his friend the lion, sometimes alone. He enjoyed his freedom more and more, and with each passing day would roam farther from his hiding place. So it came about that he was captured and taken by soldiers to the city of Rome where he was to be punished for running away from his master.

In that ancient time it was the Roman law that every runaway slave, when captured, should be

318

made to fight a hungry lion. People from far and near crowded into great arenas to see the fight. It was a cruel age.

All was made ready for the day when Androcles should fight. A savage lion was captured and shut up for a while without food. When the day came, thousands of people gathered. The emperor and all his court were there.

The roars of the lion could be heard as Androcles was unchained and led before the emperor's box. Only excitement showed in the faces of the people staring down at him. There was no pity, no kindness. Androcles stood alone in that great arena. Almost dead with fear, he made no move to defend himself as the hungry lion was let loose and came rushing toward him.

Suddenly, in the midst of his fury the lion stopped and stared at Androcles. Then he bounded forward and leaped up, rubbing his great head against the slave's face. He had recognized his friend and wanted to be petted. Flinging his arms around the lion's neck, Androcles cried for joy.

The people shouted in wonder. They could not understand what had happened. The emperor was so curious that he had Androcles brought before him and questioned.

Standing proudly with his arm around the lion's neck, Androcles told his story to the emperor. He said, "I removed a sharp thorn from this lion's wounded paw. For this kindness he fed and sheltered me. I am a man, but no man has ever befriended me. This lion is like a brother to me."

The people heard and marveled at this tale. They were so moved that they cried, "Live and be free! Live and be free!"

The emperor, pleased by the story of the faithful lion, gave Androcles his freedom and had the lion set free to return to his forest home.

*An Aesop Fable*

# The Bell of Atri

A long time ago the king of Atri bought a large bell and ordered that it be hung in a tower in the market place. A long rope was fastened to the bell, so long that even the smallest child could reach it.

"It is the bell of justice," said the king.

When at last everything was ready, the people of Atri came down to the market place to look at the bell of justice. It was a handsome bell, polished until it looked almost as bright and yellow as the sun.

"How we should like to hear it ring!" the people said.

Then the king came slowly down the street.

"Perhaps our king will ring it," said the people.

Everybody stood very still and waited to see what the king would do, but he did not ring the bell. When he came to the foot of the tower, he stopped and raised his hand.

"My people," the king said. "You see this beautiful bell. It is your bell, but you must never ring it except in case of need. If anyone of you is wronged at any time, he may come here and ring the bell. Then the judges shall come together at

321

once, hear his case, and give him justice. Rich
and poor, old and young, all alike may come.
But no one may touch the rope unless he knows
that he has been wronged."

The bell of justice hung in its place for many
years. Many times it rang out to call the judges
together. Many wrongs were righted, many ill-
doers were punished. At last the rope became
frayed from use and age. It had become so short
that only a tall man could reach it.

"This will never do," said the judges one day
as they looked at the old rope. "What if a child
should be wronged? He could not ring the bell
to let us know."

They gave orders that a new rope should be put upon the bell at once—a rope that should hang down to the ground so that the smallest child could reach it.

Such a rope could not be found in that part of Italy. The judges would have to send across the mountains for one, and it would be many days before the rope could be brought. What if some great wrong should be done before it came? How could the judges deal justice if the wronged one could not ring the bell to let them know?

"Let me fix it for you," said a man who stood by.

He ran into his garden, which was not far away, and soon came back with a long grapevine in his hands.

"This will do for a rope," he said and climbed up to fasten it to the bell. The slender vine, with its leaves and tendrils still upon it, trailed to the ground.

"Yes," said the judges, "it is a very good rope. Let it be as it is."

On the hillside above the village there lived a man who had once been a brave knight. When he was young, he had ridden through many lands, and he had fought in many a battle. Brave and

323

daring were his deeds. His best friend through all that time had been his horse—a strong, noble steed that had carried him safely through every danger and served him well.

The knight, when he grew older, cared no more to ride into battle. He thought of nothing but gold. He became a miser. At last he sold all that he had, except his horse, and went to live in a little hut on a hillside. Day after day he sat among his moneybags and planned how he might get more of the dazzling gold. Day after day his horse stood in his bare stall, half-starved and shivering with cold.

"What is the use of keeping that lazy steed?" said the miser to himself one morning. "He is old and lame and no longer able to work. I might sell him, but there is not a man who would buy a lame horse. I cannot even give him away. I shall turn him out to shift for himself. If he starves to death, so much the better."

So the brave old horse was turned out to seek what he could among the rocks on the barren hillside. Lame and sick, he wandered along the dusty roads. Cruel boys threw stones at him, dogs barked at him, and in all the world there was no one to pity him.

324

One hot afternoon, when no one was upon the street, the horse chanced to wander into the market place. Not a man or child was there, for the heat of the sun had forced them all indoors. His dim eyes saw the grapevine rope that hung from the bell of justice. The leaves and tendrils upon it were still fresh and green. What a fine dinner they would be for a starving horse!

He stretched his thin neck and took one of the slender tendrils in his mouth. It was hard to break it from the vine. He pulled at it, and the great bell began to ring. All the people in Atri heard it. It seemed to plead—

"Some one has done me wrong!
Some one has done me wrong!
Oh! come and judge my case!
Oh! come and judge my case!
For I've been wronged!"

The judges heard the
bell and hurried to the
market place. They
wondered who could be
ringing the bell at such a time.
When they passed through the gate,
they saw the old horse nibbling at the vine.

"Ha!" cried one. "It is the miser's steed. He
has come to seek justice, for his master, as
everybody knows, has been shamefully unkind to
him."

"He pleads his cause as well as any dumb beast
can," said another.

"And he shall have justice!" said a third.

In the meantime a crowd of men, women, and
children had come into the market place, eager to
learn what cause the judges were about to try.
When they saw the horse, all stood still in wonder.
Then everyone was ready to witness how he had
seen the horse wandering on the barren hills,
uncared for, while his master sat at home counting
his bags of gold.

326

"Go bring the miser before us," said the judges.

When he came, they ordered him to stand and hear their judgment.

"This horse has served you well for many a year," they said. "He has saved you from many a danger. Therefore we order that half of all your gold be set aside to buy him shelter and food, a green pasture where he may graze, and a warm stall to keep him comfortable in his old age."

The miser hung his head and grieved to lose his gold, but the people shouted with joy as the old horse was led away to a dinner such as he had not had in many a day.

*James Baldwin*

327

# William Tell

Once upon a time there lived in Switzerland a cruel ruler by the name of Gessler. In those days Switzerland was controlled by Austria. Gessler had been named to his post by the Duke of Austria, who was equally cruel.

The Duke of Austria hated the Swiss people, and Gessler hated them, too. He hated them because no matter what he did to them, the hearts of the Swiss remained brave and free.

Gessler enjoyed making the people as unhappy as possible. It sometimes seemed as if he did nothing all day long but think of new ways to bring unhappiness to the people under his rule. Therefore the Swiss in turn hated him and longed for the day when they would be free of him.

328

One day Gessler ordered his men to set up a long pole in the market place of an important village. A cap was placed on the top of the pole. It was the kind of cap worn by the Duke of Austria. Then Gessler gave orders that every man who passed by the pole must salute the cap. If he failed to give a salute, he would be punished.

Of all the orders that Gessler had given up to that time, none was so hateful to the Swiss. To be forced to salute the duke himself was bad enough. But to have to salute his cap was the final shame to their pride. Everyone kept away from the market place.

Now, living at some distance from the village, was a brave Swiss by the name of William Tell. He was a hunter whose fame with the crossbow had traveled throughout the mountainous country. He was skillful with boats too, and had had much practice in handling them upon the Swiss lakes.

It was a saying that William Tell knew how to handle the tiller of a boat as well as he did the crossbow. In short, he was a man who stood out among his fellows both for the things he could do and for his courage and intelligence. And he shared with them their hate of Gessler.

329

One day it happened that William Tell had need to go to the village. His wife was frightened when she heard of the visit her husband planned.

"Why go there, my husband?" she asked. "The place is full of danger and trouble."

To this Tell replied, "My business takes me there. I shall go forth like an honest man who is doing only what is his duty. Not yet have the Swiss become slaves. They may still dare to come and go at their will."

"Nevertheless, I should be easier in my mind if you would remain at home," said his wife.

During this conversation their son Walter was standing near by, listening closely to what his parents were saying. "May I go with you, Father?" he asked as soon as he had a chance.

"No, indeed," said the mother quickly. " 'Tis bad enough to have your father in danger."

But William Tell smiled down into his son's eager face and shook his head at his wife's words.

"The danger is largely in your own mind, my wife," he said. "I think it would be well for Walter to begin to take part in the business of men. 'Tis time my sons knew something of the sorry state of their country. It is not too soon for them to hate such men as Gessler."

330

And so the next day Walter and his father started for the village. Proudly the little boy walked along the mountain path behind his father, trying to make his short legs match his father's long strides.

William Tell swung along fearlessly, his crossbow balanced on his shoulder. His hunter's eyes watched every slope and thicket. His loyal Swiss heart burned with rage at the thought of the cap which he would be expected to salute in the village market place.

At last they reached the village. To get to the place where he wished to go, Tell had to do one of two things. He could take the direct way and cross the market place where hung the hated cap. Or he could take a roundabout route as the rest of the people had been doing.

331

For just an instant William Tell paused to make his choice. The pause lasted no longer than it takes to draw a breath.

Holding little Walter's hand, and steadying the crossbow on his shoulder, he walked boldly forward into the market place. There was no one in sight except Gessler's guards. They looked curiously at the big hunter, who walked so fearlessly with his little boy at his side.

Now Tell was close to the pole with the cap resting on its top. But still his eyes remained fixed in front of him. With one hand he still held a hand of his son. With the other he still balanced his crossbow. Three more strides and he was beside the pole.

The guards watched eagerly. Would he dare to disobey and march by? Not yet had he raised a hand in salute. How much further would he go? Now the pole and the Duke of Austria's cap were behind him, and William Tell had failed to give the salute!

Except for the steady beat of Tell's footsteps, there was complete silence in the market place for the next minute. It took the guards that long to understand that this brave Swiss really had the courage to disobey Gessler's order.

332

But after that one minute of surprise they sprang into action. With a mighty shout they closed in on Tell and little Walter and made them prisoners.

Meanwhile a crowd of villagers had gathered, and soon Gessler himself rode up to where Tell stood bravely facing the excited guards.

"What's the meaning of all this?" he demanded as the crowd parted to let him through.

"This man," said the captain of the guards, "has failed to salute the cap."

Gessler turned and looked Tell slowly up and down. "What is your name, fellow?" he asked sharply.

"William Tell."

"And this is your son?" Gessler pointed to Walter standing without fear beside his father.

"Yes," said Tell proudly.

Gessler smiled. He seemed to be in no hurry and acted almost as if he were enjoying it all. His smile was cruel.

"You know," he said, "that any disobedience to my orders is swiftly and severely punished?"

"I know," said Tell quietly.

"No doubt you are a hunter and a good shot with the bow?" he asked.

333

Before Tell could answer, a dozen voices from the crowd declared him to be the best shot in all Switzerland.

"Then," said Gessler, "he shall have a chance to show us what he can do." He looked straight into Tell's eyes and added, "Your son shall stand under that tree on the other side of the market place, and you shall shoot an apple from his head. And if you do not aim at the apple, you shall die." Then, turning to the guards, "Tie the boy to the tree," he ordered.

At once the guards seized Walter, but Tell hung onto him and held him close. He was frightened at the fearful deed he was about to do. To shoot an apple from his own boy's head at such a distance! It was impossible. Not even William Tell could shoot like that. If he missed his aim, the arrow would certainly take Walter's life.

The boy spoke for the first time since he had entered the market place. "Don't look like that, Father," he begged. "I'm not afraid, really I'm not. I know you can do it."

Tell shook his head sadly. The guards led Walter away and bound him to the tree. Then they placed an apple on the top of his head.

334

Steadfastly, the boy looked across the market place to where his father stood, his crossbow in his hands.

Slowly Tell drew two arrows from his quiver and stuck one of them into his belt. Still more slowly he wound his bow, fitted the other arrow to the string, and raised the bow to his shoulder.

And now those near him saw that William Tell had recovered from that first terrible fright. He stood firm as a rock. His eyes and hands were steady.

Not a sound came from the market place as Tell took careful aim. The watchers hardly breathed. When the arrow sped from the bow, the twang of the bowstring rang loudly in the stillness. Then a shout went up from all the villagers, for the apple was split cleanly in two. With proud eyes Walter watched his father run eagerly toward him.

In a moment the guards had cut the ropes, and Tell snatched his son in his arms.

Instantly Gessler touched him on the shoulder. "I saw you take two arrows and place one of them in your belt. Tell me, what was that second arrow for?" he asked.

William Tell straightened up and looked Gessler in the eye.

336

"Had I missed the apple and killed my son, the second arrow would have been for you. I shouldn't have missed twice."

At these brave words Gessler ordered the guards to seize Tell and tie him hand and foot. "I am going to put you," he said, "where you will never see the sun or stars again."

So Tell was dragged away from the market place. The prison where he was to be locked up was across a large lake. A terrible storm arose as they were taking him across and the boat seemed sure to be wrecked. Gessler and the guards were half paralyzed with fear.

At last Gessler commanded that Tell be unbound in order that he might handle the boat, since he was the most skillful boatman in Switzerland. William Tell needed all his skill at the tiller, but he managed to get the boat to shore. There he leaped from it and made a dash for freedom. Because of the storm Gessler and his men were unable to follow quickly enough to catch him, and Tell managed to escape.

Some time later William Tell had a chance to use that second arrow. He was watching for Gessler in a mountain pass. An instant after the arrow left his crossbow, it found its resting place in Gessler's heart. With Gessler's death, Switzerland was one step nearer to freedom.

All this happened many, many years ago. But because of men like William Tell, the little country of Switzerland is today one of the most freedom-loving and peaceful countries on earth.

*A Swiss Legend*

# Robin Hood and the Sheriff

Now it happened during the rule of King John of England that a band of merry outlaws went to live in Sherwood Forest. They were led by a bold and clever man who called himself Robin Hood.

The times were bad. The cowardly king was unjust and ruled badly. Rich and cruel lords controlled him and grew fat on stolen riches. The poor were more unhappy than ever.

Robin Hood and his merry men were friends of poor folk and enemies of King John and his rich and cruel lords. Sometimes one of them, riding a fine horse and clothed in richest velvet, came through Sherwood Forest. Then Robin Hood and his band would seize the unlucky fellow. They would take the gold from his pockets and give it to the poor, who used it to buy bread and meat.

All the people roundabout loved Robin Hood and wished him well, all except King John and his followers. The king put a price upon his head, saying that whoever would bring Robin Hood before him would be given a handsome reward for his trouble.

Now among the people most anxious to catch Robin Hood and win the king's reward was the Sheriff of the town of Nottingham. Many times he had had the outlaw almost within his grasp, but each time Robin Hood had succeeded in getting the better of the Sheriff.

However, the Sheriff would not give up. At last he decided to have an archery meet in the town of Nottingham. He would give a prize of gold to the man who could draw his strong bow and send his arrow nearest to the center of the target.

340

Robin Hood was thought by many to be the best man with a bow in all England. The Sheriff was sure that he would not miss the chance to match his skill with the best archers in the country. So word was sent out that a contest was to be held and that the prize was to be a golden arrow.

When Robin heard the news, he carried it straight to all his merry men. The whole band of outlaws decided that they too would attend the Sheriff's meet. This was fearless of them, for there was a price upon all their heads.

Nottingham was a fair sight on the day of the meet. Lords and ladies from far and near had come in their richest costumes of velvet and shimmering satin. Farmers and workers of all kinds, as well as beggars and thieves, had come, also. Everyone knew why the Sheriff was holding the meet, and all hoped to see the famous outlaw and his band.

At one end of a long meadow was the target. On one side of the meadow seats had been put up for the lords and ladies. On the other side were the poor folk, who had come to watch and to pray for the safety of their friend. They were held back by ropes from crowding into the shooting range.

The archers, including the Sheriff's best man, Gill o' the Red Cap, had gathered in tents. Some said that Gill was as fine an archer as ever drew bow. Others thought he was not so fine as Robin Hood. But as yet there were among the archers none clothed in the familiar Lincoln green, the color always worn by Robin and his men.

When all was ready, the Sheriff himself rode down the field. He was mounted on a fine horse and clothed in velvet and satin in colors as rich as the rainbow. His lady, who rode beside him on a white horse, was dressed in blue velvet.

When the Sheriff and his lady were seated, he ordered his herald to blow upon his horn. At its sound the archers all came forth from their tents.

Still, though he peered to right and left, the Sheriff could see no sign of anyone dressed in Lincoln green. But he thought Robin Hood might be among the crowd somewhere, likely in disguise. So he gave the order for the contest to begin.

The archers shot, each in turn, and never before this day had there been in England such thrilling archery. The shooting was nearly perfect.

At last ten men stood upon the field for the last round. They had outshot all the others, and in a few moments the outcome of the match would be decided.

The Sheriff spoke to one of his guards. "Think you that Robin Hood is among those ten?"

"All of them are known to me except the ragged man in scarlet," replied the guard. "He has a patch over one eye, so he is half blind, and his shaggy hair is dirty and brown. You know well, my lord, that Robin Hood has two good eyes, and his hair is as golden as the sun."

343

"That is true," agreed the Sheriff. "Yonder homely beggar could never be Robin Hood."

Again the men drew bow and let the swift arrows fly at the target. And when they had finished, three men stood upon the field. One of them was the ragged stranger with the patch covering one eye.

Again the three shot, and then only the stranger and the Sheriff's own man, Gill o' the Red Cap, were left. These two must now shoot against each other.

Gill shot first. Straight flew the arrow, and a shout went up. The arrow had struck close to the center of the target and hung quivering there for all to see.

"Well done, Gill!" cried the Sheriff. And to the half-blind stranger he called, "Forsooth, ragged rascal, let us see you do better than that."

The stranger said nothing, but took his place. No one spoke. It seemed as if no one breathed, so great was the silence. The stranger stood motionless, his one good eye measuring the distance between him and the target. Then he drew his long bow. For an instant he held it tightly drawn, then freed the arrow from the bow. Straight it flew and true, to the very center of the target.

344

No shout went up. No word was spoken as each man gazed into his neighbor's eyes and marveled how such a shot could be. The archers were silent before such shooting. At last said one, "No man is the equal of yonder stranger, whoever he may be."

Then the herald blew upon his horn, and the Sheriff came forward to give the golden arrow to the stranger, for he had won it fairly before all the people. Having done this, the Sheriff turned and marched away. Everyone could see that he was angry, and they knew why. Robin Hood had not come to the shooting. The meet had been useless, since once more the Sheriff had failed to get his man and the king's reward for his capture.

Later that day, a ragged stranger in scarlet, with a patch over one eye, came to a spreading tree deep in Sherwood Forest. There he joined an anxiously waiting band of men, who had reached the spot before him. In his hand was the golden arrow which he had lately won. Then, while his loyal companions laughed to see him, he took the patch from his eye and the ragged clothes from his body. He stood before them clothed in Lincoln green.

"Now," he said, "someone tell me how to get this brown stain as easily from my hair."

Then the merry band shouted with laughter. For it was Robin Hood himself who had won the Sheriff's golden arrow.

That very day the Sheriff sat at the head of a banquet table. On either side sat lords and ladies.

"That Robin Hood is a rascal and a coward, or he would have come to the archery meet this day," said the Sheriff, and all the others agreed.

346

But no sooner had he finished speaking than there was a loud twang and something sped through the open window. It fell upon the table right under the Sheriff's nose. He slowly lifted it, and all could see that it was an arrow with a gray goose shaft. And tied to the shaft with a silken cord was a thin roll of paper.

The Sheriff unrolled the paper, and as he read the message, his face grew dark with rage, for these words were written there:

"May blessings shower on you this day,
  Say all in sweet Sherwood,
  For you did give the prize away
  To merry Robin Hood."

*An Old English Story*

# Hiawatha's Hunting

Then Iagoo, the great boaster,
He the marvelous storyteller,
He the traveler and the talker,
He the friend of old Nokomis,
Made a bow for Hiawatha;
From a branch of ash he made it,
From an oak bough made the arrows,
Tipped with flint, and winged with feathers,
And the cord he made of deerskin.
Then he said to Hiawatha:
"Go, my son, into the forest,
Where the red deer herd together,
Kill for us a famous roebuck,
Kill for us a deer with antlers!"
Forth into the forest straightway
All alone walked Hiawatha
Proudly, with his bow and arrows;
Up the oak tree, close beside him,
Sprang the squirrel, *Adjidaumo*,
In and out among the branches,
Coughed and chattered from the oak tree,
Laughed, and said between his laughing,
"Do not shoot me, Hiawatha!"

But he heeded not, nor heard him,
For his thoughts were with the red deer;
On their tracks his eyes were fastened,
Leading downward to the river,
To the ford across the river,
And as one in slumber walked he.

Hidden in the alder bushes,
There he waited till the deer came,
Till he saw two antlers lifted,
Saw two eyes look from the thicket,
Saw two nostrils point to windward,
And a deer came down the pathway,
Flecked with leafy light and shadow.
And his heart within him fluttered,
Trembled like the leaves above him,
Like the birch leaf palpitated,
As the deer came down the pathway.

Then, upon one knee uprising,
Hiawatha aimed an arrow;
Scarce a twig moved with his motion,
Scarce a leaf was stirred or rustled,
But the wary roebuck started,
Stamped with all his hoofs together,
Listened with one foot uplifted,
Leaped as if to meet the arrow;

Ah! the singing, fatal arrow,
Like a wasp it buzzed and stung him!
   Dead he lay there in the forest,
By the ford across the river;
Beat his timid heart no longer,
But the heart of Hiawatha
Throbbed and shouted and exulted,
As he bore the red deer homeward,
And Iagoo and Nokomis
Hailed his coming with applauses.
   From the red deer's hide Nokomis
Made a cloak for Hiawatha,
From the red deer's flesh Nokomis
Made a banquet to his honor.
All the village came and feasted,
All the guests praised Hiawatha,
Called him Strong-Heart, *Soan-ge-taha!*
Called him Loon-Heart, *Mahn-go-taysee!*

*Henry Wadsworth Longfellow*

# Things to Think About and Do

1. Name the story from this unit that matches each of the following: a myth, a legend, an old story, a fable. Use the table of contents.

2. Describe how each of the underlined characters felt in the following sentences:

<u>Alexander</u> reined in the spirited stallion, which now seemed tame as a kitten.

"Wolf!" yelled the <u>boy</u>. "A wolf indeed!" But no one paid him any heed.

Suddenly, in the midst of his fury the lion stopped and stared at <u>Androcles</u>.

The <u>guards</u> watched eagerly. Would William Tell dare to march by?

"Well, whatever is in it is none of our business," said <u>Epimetheus</u>.

3. Tell how each of the following was important in a story or poem in this unit:

| | | |
|---|---|---|
| an apple | a golden arrow | a box |
| a grapevine | a black stallion | a wolf |
| a bell | an arena | a cap |

4. Which story in this unit does each of these sayings fit? Explain how it fits.

> The miser's bag is never full.
> To the grateful give more than he asks.
> Hope is grief's best music.

352

5. Copy the list of countries below, then **match** each country with a story in this unit.

| Greece | England | Italy |
| Austria | Switzerland | Macedonia |

6. Plan a "For Sale" ad for Alexander's horse using words and phrases that describe him in "A Horse Afraid of His Shadow."

7. Choose one of these possible endings for "Androcles and the Lion." Write a paragraph telling why you like the ending you chose.

The lion was given to Androcles for a pet.
The lion was put in a cage in the park.
The lion was set free to return to the forest.
The lion became a pet of the emperor's court.

8. Pretend you are Walter Tell. Write your story of how the apple was shot from your head and of what happened to you after your father was seized.

9. Copy these sentences. Write *T* in front of those that describe William Tell, and *H* if Robin Hood is described. Write *T* and *H* if both are described.

He was a skilled boatman.
He was bold and he loved freedom.
He was an outlaw who lived in the forest.
He wanted the Swiss to be free.
He was a good archer.

353

# Some Books to Read

*The Arabian Nights*, by Amabel Williams-Ellis.

Here are Aladdin, Sindbad, and other favorite characters from these great tales in a fine new retelling. There are beautiful pictures too.

*The Odyssey of Homer*, by Barbara Leonie Picard.

A Greek hero on his way home from the Trojan War has many exciting adventures.

*It's Perfectly True*, by Hans Christian Andersen.

Twenty-eight tales from one of the world's best storytellers, translated by Paul Leyssac. Among them are "The Little Mermaid" and "Thumbelina."

*Some Merry Adventures of Robin Hood*, by Howard Pyle.

The whole story of how the famous outlaw and his faithful band of followers enjoy life in Sherwood Forest.

*Stories of the Gods and Heroes*, by Sally Benson.

The myths of Greece and Rome are told in a spirited way.

*Tales Told Again*, by Walter de la Mare.

Tales from Andersen, Grimm, and others are beautifully retold by a famous poet and writer.

*Thunder of the Gods*, by Dorothy Hosford.

These are thrilling tales of the Norse gods and their struggles against the Frost Giants.

# Outer Space—Fun and Fact

# Rusty's Space Ship

Susan slowed her steps as she reached the door of the Adams's garage and peered curiously inside. She saw Rusty hammering away on a bulky shape built of wooden boxes and uneven lengths of lumber.

"What are you building?" she asked.

"A space ship," Rusty answered. "Want to see it?"

Susan entered the garage eagerly.

The space ship was about eight feet long and three feet wide. It would have looked like a covered box except that boards had been nailed on one end in such a way that they reached a point. On the other end, five tin cans had been fastened in an almost straight row.

356

There was a periscope that stuck out through a hole in the top. Susan remembered that Rusty had received the periscope for Christmas several years ago.

Then Susan noticed a small glass window. And in the top was what she decided was a trap door, since there were two sets of hinges on one side.

"Well?" said Rusty, as Susan walked slowly around the ship.

"Pretty good," she said. "Is this the nose?" She nodded toward the pointed end.

"Sure," said Rusty. "Back there are the five rockets."

357

That explained the five tin cans.

"Let's see the inside," said Susan.

The trap door lifted easily. Susan climbed onto the ship and lowered herself through the hole.

There was a control panel which Rusty had got by sending in a box top and twenty-five cents. There were buttons on the panel marked "Freeze Ray, for use on comets," "Electric Ray," "Take-off," "Steady Course," and "Landing."

"What's the stuff on this shelf?" Susan asked.

"That's my equipment. Two ray guns, my outer-space books, hammer and nails, some first-aid, and of course my telescope. That's what I got for my birthday."

"I guess you keep your food over there."

"Sure. There's a box of crackers, a jar of honey, some chocolate candy, and a couple of oranges. You never know when you'll be called out on a mission."

Rusty knew, as did Susan, that he wasn't likely to be going on a mission very soon. But he wanted to be a space-ship pilot when he grew up, and until then it was fun to play at going on missions. He was always reading books about space ships, and this "play" space ship he had built was as near like those he read about as he could make it.

"I'd better get back to work," Rusty told Susan. "I have to nail on a piece of armor plate. It will deflect meteors."

"Of course," said Susan promptly. She wasn't at all sure what he meant by deflecting meteors, but she wasn't going to let him know.

Susan leaned over the side of the ship to see what Rusty was doing. He was nailing on a piece of metal, but she couldn't imagine where it had come from or what it could have been used for. It was perfectly round and about four feet across. She noticed that the nails seemed to go through it without too much trouble, and that Rusty could bend the metal easily.

"What is that?" she asked.

"I don't know. I found it."

"Where?"

"In the city dump. Pete and I rode out there on our bikes yesterday to see if we could find anything we could use, and I found this. The minute I saw it I knew it was just what I needed for armor plate for my space ship."

Suddenly they both looked startled. From the open garage doorway they had received a message. No one had spoken aloud, yet there was no doubt about the meaning of the words.

"There's the saucer," came the message. "There's Gwump's saucer. By the rings of Saturn, I've been lucky this time."

Openmouthed with surprise, the children stared at the strange and comic figure in the doorway.

He was not over three feet high, and the fur coat he wore dragged on the ground. They could not see his face, for a man's hat was pulled down over his ears. Its brim dropped low over his nose. In one hand he carried a leather bag, and in the other a round piece of silvery metal which dragged behind him as he walked. It looked exactly like the piece of metal Rusty had just finished nailing onto the space ship.

360

"What are you doing in my mother's fur coat," Susan demanded sternly, "and my father's fishing hat? They were hanging on our clothesline to air out. I saw them there myself just a little while ago."

The stranger did not answer. Instead he advanced to the space ship and reached toward the silvery disk. When it did not come loose in his hand, they instantly had the feeling that he was worried.

"What's the matter with the thing?" they seemed to hear him say in a perplexed voice. "It's attached itself to something, someway."

He put down the bag and the piece of metal he was carrying. Then, using both hands, he tried to pull off the treasure which Rusty had found. The row of nails held fast.

"Hey," said Rusty crossly, "you leave my meteor deflector alone."

Now the stranger tipped up the hat brim and looked at them for the first time.

"Who are you?" They didn't really hear his voice, but it was surprising how clearly they heard the question.

"I'm Rusty Adams. And this is Susan Clinton. Who are you?"

"I am Tiphia, servant to Mighty Gwump. I have come for his saucer. If you hold it by some Earth magic unknown to me, I command you to break the spell."

"Sue," gasped Rusty in astonishment, "we can't hear anything, but I know what he's saying. He must be a little man from outer space."

All at once Tiphia seemed to wilt. Before he had been trying to frighten them. Now they knew he was the one who was frightened.

"Please, please," came the message from Tiphia. "Give me Gwump's saucer. This is my first assignment. My very first assignment. I can't fail."

"Even if I wanted to give it back to you," said Rusty, "I couldn't. It's nailed on too tight. Besides, I need it for a meteor deflector."

"Then," Tiphia's message came to them, "then I will take it along with whatever that thing is it's nailed onto."

"Oh, no you don't," said Rusty, and scrambled up and into the space ship.

Susan scrambled right in after him.

Just before she disappeared down the open hatch, Susan saw that Tiphia was doing something to the metal disk nailed onto the nose of the space ship. "He's trying to get it loose again," she told

362

herself. "Poor thing. It really must belong to him, or he wouldn't have another one just like it."

A moment later Tiphia lowered himself down the hatch and clamped the lid shut. At the same moment the space ship gave a shudder which threw them back on the floor. The next thing they knew, they were moving out of the garage and climbing swiftly. There was a sudden rush as if all the winds of heaven were blowing past their ears. Then Rusty and Susan knew nothing at all.

363

Some time later Rusty's eyes opened.

"Thank goodness you two are coming around," went Tiphia's thought message. "I was getting lonely sitting here all by myself."

"Where are we?" Susan's small voice asked in a frightened whisper.

"We're coming in on the Earth's only moon in a moment or so," Tiphia told her. "We are on our way to the Mighty Gwump. You wouldn't give me the other half of his flying saucer, so I had to bring you along with it. We'll stop on the moon first and give you a bit of a rest."

"How could we fly so high as the moon?" demanded Rusty. "There's no atmosphere there. We couldn't breathe."

"While you were blacked out," Tiphia told him, "I gave you a special liquid to drink. You won't need to breathe while it's in effect."

Rusty's eyes were getting used to the darkness of outer space. He could not distinguish the pieces of equipment inside the ship, but there was a suggestion of light coming through the window. He pressed his nose against the glass.

Straight ahead was the moon. It had been one of his favorite studies through the new telescope, but never had he been able to see it so clearly. It seemed to be so close that he could reach out and touch it, a great shining ball hanging in a dark sky. There were the dark and light spots which his astronomy books had told him were craters and dry plains and mountain ridges.

Tiphia had taken off the fur coat and cap. Now he looked something like a lizard only his back legs were longer than the ordinary lizard's. He was, of course, much larger, too. He was bright green in color.

Susan took a long look at the strange creature and said, "I want to go home. You turn this space ship around right now and take me home."

"Gwump will send you home as soon as he gets that metal off the ship," Tiphia told her. "He'll have to. You wouldn't care for it on Eopee, which is Gwump's planet. It will only mean another hour or so. Surely you will give me that much time. Then I will have accomplished my mission and be given another assignment."

"Oh, come on, Sue, be a sport," begged Rusty, who very much wanted to land on the moon.

"Do you promise we will be sent home right away and not harmed in any way?" Susan demanded of Tiphia.

"By the rings of Saturn I promise it," returned Tiphia.

"All right," said Susan slowly, and was rewarded by a pleased grin from Rusty, which made her feel better.

The space ship now began settling toward the strangest land they had ever seen. Everything was gray. There was no other color. The space ship landed, then seemed to change its mind, for it bounced up and down several times. Finally it settled back and remained still. Then the mountains and the plain which they could see from the window stopped moving back and forth. They had arrived on the moon.

"It's perfectly safe here. Do get out," urged Tiphia. "Only take care to have your moon legs under you."

Rusty could hardly wait to open the hatch. Susan and he jumped to the ground, and both of them bounced when their feet struck.

"What are we bouncing this way for?" asked Susan.

"It's gravity or something," explained Rusty in delight. "I read all about it in my astronomy book. We don't weigh as much here as we do at home. Come on. This will be fun."

It was fun to walk on the moon, for with each Earth step, they soared a foot or so into the air. By this time Tiphia was beside them. He walked upright, even though he was shaped like a lizard. He kept his tail curled like a round doughnut on his back.

"Nice, isn't it?" he asked. "Much nicer than walking on Earth where the land doesn't help you at all, and the first thing you know you're all tired out. Just relax and hop."

Tiphia showed them the easiest way to get around. You merely stood with two feet together and hopped. When you landed on the ground, the force carried you forward in another hop.

367

Walking was no trouble at all. It was like standing in one place and letting the ground do the work.

Rusty had been busy looking around. "What made that big crater over there?" he asked.

Tiphia shrugged his scaled shoulders. "Gwump would know . . . Gwump knows everything. But I never heard him mention that crater."

"I don't suppose he ever said anything about there being a man on the moon either," said Susan.

"No, he didn't. But you could call out. If there is a man here, and he answers, you'll know."

368

"Don't be so silly," said Rusty scornfully. "You know there isn't a man on the moon. It's just something they tell little kids. I should think, now that you've seen the place, you'd know without asking. No one could live here."

"I suppose not," she agreed meekly.

Tiphia now told them that they must return to the space ship. They had wasted quite enough time on the moon, and since they had agreed there was nothing more to see, they must continue on their journey to Eopee.

Rusty scrambled up the side of the space ship and through the open hatch.

Before Susan climbed up, she turned to Tiphia. "Please," she said, "I've got to try it. I'll never be back on the moon as long as I live. I'll never have another chance to see if there's a man on it. I'll have to try your way."

369

She cupped her hands around her mouth and called toward the distant mountains, for there was certainly no use in calling toward the empty plain.

"Hello," she called. "Hello, hello!"

For a long minute she stood waiting in silence, then back from the dark mountains came a far-away answer.

"Hello—hello!"

"Its an echo," decided Rusty instantly. "Only that's funny. How can there be an echo when there's no atmosphere to echo in?"

"Where are you?" called Susan, paying no attention to Rusty. After a moment, "Where—are —you?" the thin voice repeated.

"That's enough," urged Tiphia. "Come along. Come along. My mission must be accomplished."

"All right," agreed Susan unwillingly. But she had to have one last word with the distant voice. As she climbed up the space ship, she screamed as loudly as she could, "Good-by, Mister Moon!"

Tiphia followed her up the side and into the ship. Just before he turned to close the hatch behind him, the last words from the mountains of the moon came to them quite clearly.

"Good-by. Good-by. Come back again!"

*Evelyn Sibley Lampman*

# Danny Dunn and
# the Anti-gravity Paint

Space Captain Daniel Dunn stood on the bridge of the *Revenge* with his eyes on the viewer screens. He could see the flaming tails that were the rocket ships from Jupiter.

Adjutant Dan Dunn ran up to report. "Sir," he cried, "they're all around us!"

"We'll fight them singlehanded. Fire away!" barked the handsome Captain.

Pilot Danny Dunn pressed the firing lever.

"We'll ram them!" Captain Dunn cried. He seized the controls and swung the *Revenge* directly at the nearest enemy rocket ship.

CRASH! And down went the Captain, the Adjutant, and the Pilot.

"Daniel Dunn! What are you doing?"

The voice was that of his teacher, Miss Arnold.

The rocket ship control panel vanished. So did the enemy ships. Danny found himself sitting on the floor of his classroom. His eyes cleared, and he looked into Miss Arnold's twinkling brown eyes.

"Uh—nothing, Miss Arnold," he mumbled.

"Nothing!" said the teacher. "Do you call groaning and moaning and falling flat on the floor nothing? Don't you feel well?"

"No, ma'am. I mean, sure, I feel fine," Danny stammered.

"Get back in your seat then," Miss Arnold said, and her voice softened. "What were you doing? You certainly weren't doing arithmetic."

"I—I was thinking," he replied.

"Thinking?"

"Yes'm."

"Are you in the habit of falling down when you think?"

The class laughed. Danny felt his face redden.

Eddie Philips raised his hand. "I think I can tell you where he was. He was in a rocket ship. He's always playing something like that."

Miss Arnold tried to hide a smile.

"Is that true, Danny?" she asked.

372

He nodded meekly.

"Hm," she murmured, then said, "I know it's hard for plain old-fashioned arithmetic to stand up to rocket ships. But trips to Mars are far in the future. Meantime, you stick to the present."

"Yes, Ma'am," said Danny, "but Professor Bullfinch says that space travel may come in the next ten years."

"I have great respect for Professor Bullfinch," said Miss Arnold firmly. "But if you don't make better grades in arithmetic, you'll never become a fine scientist like him. I must think of some way to keep you on earth. Since nothing else has worked, this time I'm going to try an old-fashioned punishment. Write one hundred times, 'I will not daydream about space flights in class.' Let me see your sentences in the morning."

373

Danny pulled his mind away from outer space and went back to arithmetic.

Dan's father had died when Danny was a baby. Since then his mother had worked for Professor Euclid Bullfinch. The Professor lived alone and needed Mrs. Dunn to keep house for him.

Danny usually went right to the Professor's laboratory to spend some time after school. But today his mother called as he entered the house.

"How did things go today, Danny?" she asked.

"All right," he answered, trying to grin, as he went into the kitchen to talk with her.

"Daniel Dunn," said his mother, "whenever I see that sickly smile, I know you've been up to something. What happened?"

"Well, I—I have to write a hundred sentences."

"Humph! I can guess. 'I will not fight with people in the halls!' Is that it?"

"No. 'I will not daydream about space flight in class,'" answered Danny.

"Danny Dunn," said Mrs. Dunn severely, "stay right here in the kitchen where I can keep an eye on you until you get those sentences done. Now I know what your teacher meant when she said, 'Danny's trying to fly before he can walk.' Space flying!"

374

Professor Bullfinch came into the kitchen just as Danny was getting paper. "Can you spare Danny for a few minutes?" he asked. "I would like to take him into the laboratory."

"I can spare him," said Mrs. Dunn, "but his schoolwork can't. He has to write 'I will not daydream about space flight in class' one hundred times."

"He dreamed one hundred times about the same thing?" asked the Professor.

"No! He has to write that a hundred times."

"Oh! Why doesn't the school let him use a mimeograph machine? It would be much quicker."

"It's a punishment," said Mrs. Dunn patiently.

"A punishment for daydreaming about space flight? It's because scientists daydreamed about space flight that we have satellites above us now. Great guns! Satellites. Come along Danny."

Mrs. Dunn shook her head and put the paper for Danny's sentences on a shelf.

The Professor led Danny to the telescope. He looked at the time, then adjusted the instrument.

"Look!" he said. "You can see our new satellite."

Danny peered through the eyepiece. "It looks like a moon," he said. "I wish I could be on it to see what the earth looks like from up there."

375

"A good idea," the Professor laughed as he answered. "A scientist must always be asking, 'How? What? Why?' I've been asking myself those questions all day—especially 'Why?' "

"Why what?"

The Professor pointed to a laboratory bench. On it was a metal stand on which there was a glass beaker. It contained a curious liquid that glowed and quivered as if it were full of sunlight.

"I've been working on an insulating paint for rockets," he said. "I was so sure I had it that I invited two scientists from the American Rocket Society to come see it this afternoon. But the liquid has begun to quiver and I don't know why."

Danny leaned forward. "Listen, Professor," he said eagerly, reaching for the beaker. "Maybe . . ."

His fingers jerked nervously.

"Look out!" cried the Professor, as the beaker crashed to the floor.

Danny stared in horror as the quivering stuff dripped from the edge of the bench and formed a pool on the floor. He felt too miserable to look up at the Professor right away, but when he did, he saw that the Professor's face was as round and calm as ever.

"Accidents will happen, Dan," he said kindly.

376

Working fast, they scooped up as much of the liquid as they could and had almost finished when the guests arrived. They left the clean-up job and went into the living room to greet the two men from the Rocket Society.

The Professor stepped forward to welcome them. He started to shake hands with the first man, Mr. Willoughby, but as their fingers touched, there was a faint crackle. Mr. Willoughby snatched his hand away.

"Oh!" said the Professor, "I'm . . ."

Before he could say another word he shot right up off the floor. There was a dull thud as his head banged against the ceiling.

For a moment there was complete silence. Then Mr. Willoughby said weakly, "Professor, what are you standing on?"

"It is difficult," the Professor replied, "to say whether I am hanging, floating, or lying upwards, but I'm certainly not standing."

Dr. Grimes, the other visitor, and a most serious one, commanded, "Professor Euclid Bullfinch, come down at once. It is hardly fitting for a man of your position to be up there."

378

The Professor raised his arms and pushed against the ceiling. He pushed himself down to arm's length. The instant he stopped pushing, however, and dropped his arms, he bounced back up against the ceiling.

"Ow!" he yelled. "Drat it!"

"It's a trick," yelled Dr. Grimes. "He can't fool me. I'll soon get him down."

He reached up and caught hold of the Professor's legs. It was hard work, but red-faced and puffing, he managed to pull the Professor down a few feet.

"There!" he said, letting go of the Professor.

And the Professor soared upwards again. This time he protected his head with his arms.

"I'm still here, Dr. Grimes," he called.

Danny had been too startled to talk. But now he called out, "Professor, you know what?"

"Yes, I know what," said the Professor. "I'm getting a stiff neck from trying to look down."

At this point Danny shouted, "But Professor, I'm trying to tell you! The soles of your shoes —they're glowing and quivering! Just like that insulating stuff in the beaker! You must have stepped in it when we were cleaning up!"

Climbing on a chair, Danny reached up and untied the Professor's shoes.

379

"Wait a minute!" cried the Professor, as Danny slipped both his shoes off. "For I think . . ."

The shoes flew out of Danny's hands and stuck to the ceiling. The weird glow could be plainly seen on their soles.

". . . we have conquered gravity!" the Professor shouted, and crashed to the floor.

Groaning a little, Professor Bullfinch got to his feet. Then, standing on a chair, he took hold of one of the shoes, and with much pulling, forced it away from the ceiling.

"Danny," he called. "Open a window, please. Quickly for I can't hold this shoe much longer."

The others opened another window to watch.

380

Professor Bullfinch held the shoe out the window and opened his hand. The shoe rose swiftly into the evening air, catching the last rays of the sun on its surface, and then vanished from their sight.

"How did you do it?" cried Mr. Willoughby.

"I'm not sure," said the Professor. "But I believe that we may have the answer to the problem of space flight with this anti-gravity paint."

Danny's eyes widened. "S-space flight!" he shouted.

It was nearly eleven when he went up to bed. Before climbing in, he opened the window and looked out. Above him the sky sparkled with stars. Somewhere among those glowing, twinkling points of light, one of Professor Bullfinch's shoes sailed on and out, away from the familiar earth.

"A ship to the stars," murmured Danny.

*Jay Williams and Raymond Abrashkin*

381

# Castaways in Space

Skip and Glen had wanted more than anything else to become space pilots and to fly the great rocket ships from Earth to Mars. But they had failed their tests as space cadets, and the best they could hope for was to be sent to Mars as members of a ground crew. Now they were in a space ship nearing Mars. They were ready to begin their work, yet neither boy was happy about it.

All would have gone well on the flight if the ship hadn't given that sudden lurch. No one in the crew was hurt when thrown from his place by this sudden movement of the plane. But Skip was pushing a supply case against the door of the plane's chute at the time. He was knocked against the lever which opened the door. The door shot up and a big square of black space opened before his eyes.

In the next instant Skip was following the supply case down the chute. Quickly Glen stretched his body full length to grasp Skip's space suit before he could leave the ship. But Skip was skidding too fast. Suddenly, Glen felt himself sliding helplessly. There was no time to warn the rest of the crew. Before he knew it, Glen was out

382

in space, alone with Skip. Skip now looked like
a toy balloon as he drifted through the vacuum.
Castaways in space. That's what they were.

"Skip," Glen called over his space-suit radio.
"Do you hear me, Skip?"

"Yes, Glen," Skip's reply was hardly more
than a faint squeak.

Glen looked down and ahead where a huge rock
some ten miles across hung in the starry darkness.

"If we can make Phobos, we may be all right. She doesn't have any gravity to speak of, and we may be able to land on her."

"We won't make Phobos," Skip replied faintly. "We'll either run into Mars' gravity field and crash on it, or float through space until our air runs out."

"Be quiet, Skip, and listen to me." Glen's voice was sharp. "See if you can pick up a little speed by kicking out behind. Work your feet and hands as if you were swimming. Try to catch up with the supply case. If you reach it, hang on."

Skip didn't reply, but Glen saw his arms and legs begin to move. Glen worked his own. It was hard work, but Glen found that he was able to increase his speed in much the same way that a space ship makes its way through the sky. By the time Glen touched Skip's suit, both of them were breathing freely of their precious oxygen.

"What's the idea?" Skip asked as his gloved hand clutched the strap of the supply case and Glen held onto him.

"We'll use the case to break our fall," Glen explained. "Remember, it's covered with anti-contact rubber so that it won't go to pieces when it hits."

384

The two had been preparing to drop the emergency supply case on Mars when Skip had lurched against that lever. Glen was glad they had put on their space suits before the accident. He saw that the space ship was now only a tiny needle against the red circle of Mars. He and Skip had likely not even been missed by the crew. When the boys did find out that he and Skip were gone, they wouldn't know where to look for them.

"I believe we *are* going to make it," Skip said suddenly.

Phobos was a rough looking, frightening giant below, but Glen held nothing but love for it. Their speed had increased a little, but it did not look as if they would hit the ground fast enough to be killed.

Glen felt Skip's muscles tighten for the landing.

"Steady, fellow!" he said quietly.

Then he felt a rough jar, and he bounced off Skip's back as though he were rubber. Glen spread out his arms to ease his fall, then was surprised to find his body settling down to rest as lightly as a leaf.

"We have hardly any weight at all," he said.

Skip had almost drifted off into space again, but Glen grabbed his leg and pulled him back.

"It's a crazy world, isn't it?" Skip said, as he explored the rocky scene that sloped down from them on both sides. It was strange to be on a globe so tiny you could even see its roundness.

Glen nodded. "We've really got to keep both feet on the ground here."

"What if they don't find us, Glen?" Skip asked gloomily. "What then?"

"I don't know, Skip," Glen sighed. "Let's see what's in the supply case."

Glen was able to crawl better than he could walk over to the supply case. Skip followed. Glen pressed a button on the case and the top sprang up.

386

"There's not much that isn't here!" said Skip, peering inside. "Oxygen tanks, a bubble tent, food capsules, water maker, first-aid, flares, books, electronic stove-heater."

"Let's put up the bubble tent," Glen said. "It will save our heat."

Glen went to work as he had learned to do during his cadet training. He took a tube from the case and pulled a lever. The tube popped open and a plastic bubble began growing out of it. The bubble grew to about seven feet, then loosened itself from the airtight tube. After it had hardened for several minutes, Glen took an electric saw and cut a small door in the side. Then Skip made hinges from self-sealing plastic strips.

387

They used the anticontact rubber from around the case for a floor, and put the food capsules and other supplies inside the bubble. Then they switched on the electronic heater and turned off the heat in their suits.

"How long do you think our supplies can last, Glen?" Skip asked.

"They're supposed to last two people ten days," Glen replied.

Skip laughed. "You talk as if we had a lifetime ahead of us. We don't know whether we've got *tomorrow*."

"Which reminds me, we'd better send off some flares to let somebody know where we are." Glen picked up some of the rocket flares and floated out of the bubble again. He set up a flare on its three legs, pointed it at Mars' red surface, and pulled on the release catch. But it wouldn't move.

"It's jammed!" Glen tried another rocket and it acted in the same way. Then another, and another. They were all useless, all the release catches were bent, possibly from having been kept too near a heat outlet in the ship.

"How will we signal Mars now?" Skip asked.

"Anything we throw out will be drawn to the planet by its own gravity," Glen answered.

388

"How about throwing out some of the extra supplies?" Skip asked. "We can attach a note."

"It's a good suggestion, but there is very little chance that they'd be found. Only a small part of Mars has people on it. No, I'm afraid we'd wait here forever if we had to count on that."

"But what else is there to do?" Skip's eyes were round with sudden fear.

Glen frowned to hide his own growing fear. "It looks as though we'd have to get to Mars on our own ship," he said.

"We'd be broken to bits!"

"Not the way I plan to do it," said Glen. He scrambled into the bubble tent and came out with an engineering book. Skip watched as Glen began working some problems on the rock with a piece of stone.

After a while Glen said, "I think it'll work, Skip. Want to take a chance?"

"I'd like to know what it is first."

"We can use the parachute from the supply case and attach it to the bubble," Glen explained. "Then we can ride in the bubble to Mars."

"It sounds completely crazy," said Skip.

"At least it's better than sitting here and just hoping we'll be found. Shall we try it?"

Skip shrugged. "If it's our only chance, I'm willing."

They set to work taping the lines of the parachute around and under the plastic bubble. They used more of the plastic strips to fasten the lines tightly. The boys decided to carry as few supplies as possible to make their weight lighter. When they were ready to go, they climbed into the bubble, and Glen pushed them off with one foot outside the door.

"We'll seal ourselves in airtight with the strips," he said, pulling the door shut. "That'll hold our vacuum in and help keep us light when we get into the atmosphere of Mars."

"How long do you think it will take us to get there?" asked Skip.

"I figured about a hundred hours," said Glen. "If that doesn't put us close to Mars City, we should be able to reach some other settlement."

They moved slowly at first. Glen hoped for only enough speed to carry them into Mars' gravity pull. As they neared the red planet, their speed would increase and that worried Glen. If they gained too much speed and struck Mars' air blanket too fast, the parachute might be ripped from the bubble.

To while away the many hours, the boys napped and took turns reading the one storybook they had brought along. On the third day they could see the canals on Mars. On the fourth day they could see the buildings of Mars City.

"Cross your fingers, Skip, our parachute should open in the next few minutes."

What if it didn't? Then they would end up in little pieces on Mars' red earth or maybe in a canal. While he was thinking of this, Glen felt a sharp drag and was tumbled over onto Skip.

"Look!" cried Skip, pointing overhead. "The parachute's open!"

Some minutes later, the red ground rushed up at them. Glen's muscles tightened and his heart thumped rapidly as the last few hundred feet melted away. He was glad they had the anti-contact rubber cushion beneath them.

392

As they struck, Glen was thrown against the top of the bubble. Plastic clattered as the bubble rolled over and over. When it stopped, Glen straightened himself out. He was shaken up but he was unhurt. He looked at Skip.

"We made it," Glen said, in a shaking voice. He tore off the door seals, pushed out the door, and let the air of Mars rush into the vacuum of their bubble. Then they got out and stretched their legs. Looking at Mars City in the distance, Glen asked, "Ready to start walking?"

Less than an hour later, an astonished captain at the Mars City space port heard the boys' story.

"Your courage and quick thinking are fine and unusual," the captain said when they had finished. "I can't believe that you two failed to make the cadets. If you didn't fail because you were unable to learn, I am sure we can make arrangements to give you another chance."

"We didn't fail because we couldn't learn the lessons. We failed for another reason," Skip said.

"What reason was that?" demanded the captain.

"We failed the test to find out whether or not we would know what to do in an emergency!" explained Glen.

*Richard Elam, Jr.*

393

# Faster Than Sound

It was a hot summer day in 1951. Heat waves shimmered across the sand of the California desert. But inside the big four-engined B–29 bomber, cruising at 20,000 feet, it was cold.

"It's time to get in, Bill," someone said and pointed to the *Skyrocket*, a Douglas D–558–2.

Bill Bridgeman looked at the aircraft. It looked more like something out of a Buck Rogers comic strip than a craft in which a man could really fly. Its white shape lay in the specially-built bomb bay of the B–29. Bill swallowed nervously and wondered what was in store for him. Today he would try to go faster than man had ever gone before. He would try to go higher, too.

He climbed into the small cockpit and plugged his pressurized suit into the lines. Then he plugged in the oxygen, radio, and electric heating. He felt pretty much like just another instrument.

The B–29 crew clamped the cockpit lid over him. Bill tested the pressure in the four rocket tubes that furnished the *Skyrocket* its only power. Those four rockets carried more power than man had ever before put into an airplane of the *Skyrocket's* size. They would gobble up a ton of fuel a minute, and Bill carried just four minutes' worth. By now the B–29 was 35,000 feet up. It was time for the break-away signal.

The B–29 pilot gave the signal, "5—4—3—2—1."

The *Skyrocket* dropped away from its mother ship. Someone gave the good-luck sign. But Bill didn't see it.

He was busy working the rocket switches. Numbers 1, 2, 3, and 4 rockets flamed into action. The *Skyrocket* leaped forward. Bill pulled back on the controls and pointed the nose straight up into the bright blue sky.

He was climbing, yet within ten seconds he was going faster than the speed of sound, which is around 760 miles per hour. Even the roar of the rockets dropped behind. Bill was flying in complete silence.

In spite of his heated suit, it began to get cold. Outside the *Skyrocket* the temperature was 67 degrees below zero.

Climbing, climbing, climbing. Bill was heading straight for the sun. He didn't know how high he was. He didn't have time to watch the many instruments in front of him. But out of the small window he caught a glimpse of the curving horizon of a round world. You had to be mighty high to see the curve of the horizon.

With less than a minute's worth of fuel left, Bill leveled off for his speed run. He fed the rockets every ounce of fuel they would take. The *Skyrocket* cut through the thin upper atmosphere at twice the speed of a bullet.

Bill held his mouth firm and let her go. Suddenly the plane began to buck and skid like a wild horse. Hopefully, Bill eased the controls first one way, then the other. The *Skyrocket* obeyed his movements and settled down.

Then the last ounce of fuel coughed through her rocket tubes. The *Skyrocket* slowed back down into the world of sound, where Bill could speak his thanks, and hear himself doing it.

Without power, Bill started gliding downward, hoping he could find the strip to make a landing. Then halfway down he saw a *Saberjet* cruising around, just waiting for him. It was a welcome sight.

397

"Relax, Bill," the pilot of the *Saberjet* called over the radio. "I'll show you home. Where have you been? Did you go out for a sandwich?"

"I've been playing tag with the stars," Bill radioed back.

And so he had.

Later, after Bill was safely on the ground, engineers studied the various instrument recordings. They were amazed at the story that these figures told.

"Bill," one said, "you flew higher than anyone has ever gone before. You went over 79,000 feet in the air. Almost 15 miles *up!*"

"And," another added, "you hit a speed of 1,238 miles an hour! More than twenty miles a minute! That's the fastest man has ever gone. Congratulations!"

"Bill, you are the fastest man in the world, the highest flying human being who ever lived! How does it feel, boy?" called a third engineer.

Bill Bridgeman knew how good it felt to have his feet on the ground. As for being the fastest man, he knew that a new and more powerful rocket plane was already waiting to be tested. Records are made to be broken.

*Charles Coombs*

# Explorer Is in Orbit

It was a January evening at the Atlantic Missile Range, at Cape Canaveral, Florida. A large rocket which had been ready for days was going through the final count-down. The rocket was a Jupiter-C, designed by Dr. Wernher von Braun. It had the job of carrying the first American-made satellite into orbit around the earth.

399

The launching crew was in the blockhouse checking instruments which told them everything that went on in the rocket. The various range stations were checking in by radio-telephone. These range stations would follow the path of the rocket from the time it was fired. They would receive and report information sent by instruments in the rocket.

The Missile Range was known as Station One, and when the men talked over the radio from there they would say, "This is Station One," or just, "This is One." Station Two was also in Florida, at a place called Jupiter Inlet.

Station Three was on Grand Bahama Island, and other stations were spread out along the chain of Bahama islands.

There was one station on Puerto Rico and the farthest of all was Station Twelve on a tiny British-owned island in the middle of the South Atlantic Ocean.

The stations checked in one by one.

"Four,—Ready."

"Six,—Ready."

"Three,—Ready."

At times there were questions back and forth. "This is One. Is your signal steady, Station Five?"

"I am reading it and it's holding pretty steady," came the answer from Station Five.

The safety officers had done several other things in the meantime. They had seen to it that no military aircraft would try to land on the airstrip at the cape until after the rocket had been launched and was streaking toward its orbit.

They had also called all airlines which fly into Florida. Nonstop flights between Miami and New York usually cut across water and pass over the ocean where the rocket might fly. If everything went well, the airliners would be flying at ten thousand feet while the rocket would be over fifty-two thousand feet up. But when making safety arrangements one has to plan for things that may go wrong. For this reason the airliners had been told not to cross the ocean. They would fly over Florida, behind Cape Canaveral.

The time was about 9:30 P.M. and the countdown went out through the wires and over the loudspeakers:

"T minus seventy minutes and counting."

The last two words of this message were the ones which were important. When the announcer said, ". . . and counting," it meant that everything was going well.

401

If something had gone wrong somewhere, the announcer would have said, ". . . and holding."

This would have meant that everything must wait until the men had found what was wrong and had fixed it.

"T minus thirty minutes and counting."

Now things began to look lively. The liquid fuel for the main rocket had been loaded and the rocket was taking on the liquid oxygen that would be needed for burning the fuel from the first moment on. The Jupiter-C was a four-stage rocket. The main rocket, the first stage, used a liquid fuel. The other three stages used solid fuel.

Liquid oxygen looks like water that has been colored light blue. It is very cold; almost 300 degrees below zero. And because it is so cold, it boils fiercely all the time. The liquid pours into the rocket's tank, but the tank is warm. It has the temperature of the Florida air. The oxygen chills the tank and it becomes white with frost.

As the oxygen rushed into the tank, some of it boiled away, and escaped through vents. The oxygen that escaped from the vents couldn't be seen, but it was still so cold that it froze the moisture in the air. This made it look as if a plume of white steam were coming from the rocket.

Soon the whole base of the rocket was almost hidden by swirling mists of frozen moisture. Powerful searchlights were trained on the rocket so that people could see it. The searchlights made the white mist look as if it were glowing with a light of its own.

Through the swirling mists a red light flashed, on and off, on and off. To someone who did not know what was going on, it must have looked as if the rocket were on fire. The light really came from a very powerful red lamp. When it flashed as it did, it meant "stay away." It was the sign that a rocket was almost ready to be fired, and that only those men who were firing the rocket should be near. Other people should be at least one half mile away.

"T minus twenty minutes and counting."

The white mists were still swirling around the rocket, and the red light was still flashing.

Now the "basket" on top of the rocket began to spin. The "basket," as the rocket men casually called it, was really three groups of rockets inside and on top of each other. One group was made up of eleven solid-fuel rockets. These were arranged in a circle with a large hole in the middle. They would burn together, and they were called the second stage.

Inside the hole in the middle of the second stage of rockets was a smaller group which the scientists called a "cluster." The three rockets in this smaller group were solid-fuel rockets. This "cluster" formed the third stage.

404

A single rocket was on top of the "cluster." This rocket was the fourth and final stage.

"T minus nine minutes and counting."

The rocket stood brightly lighted by the search-lights. The red light was flashing. The "basket" was spinning and would keep on spinning. It would steady the rocket in the upper stages.

Everything seemed to be going well. The range stations, Jupiter Inlet, Grand Bahama, Puerto Rico—all were waiting. The scientists thought over once more what had to happen.

The first stage would carry the other stages into a large arc which should level off two hundred miles up. The upper stages would reach this

405

height still unburned. When they were at the top of the arc they would get a radio command which would start them burning. The three upper stages would burn very quickly, one after the other. The fourth stage, with the instruments in its nose, should then be traveling fast enough to go into orbit.

"T minus thirty seconds."

The white mists were nearly gone now.

"T minus twelve seconds."

"T minus 5—4—3—2—1 FIRE!"

Everyone waited for the rocket to take off. But nothing happened. The rocket just sat on its launching pad. Everything was all right, but it did not rise. Finally, after about fifteen seconds, the rocket started out. A flame shot out of its tail, grew large and bright, and the noise was like thunder, as the rocket slowly lifted from the pad.

In spite of the delay everything went well. The first stage burned and performed beautifully. Two minutes later the flame winked out. The first stage had used all of its fuel. Dr. Wernher von Braun felt that all was going well, but the upper stages still had to be fired.

It was up to Dr. Ernst Stuhlinger to give the signal. He waited, looking at his watch.

To everyone else it seemed as if the proper time had long passed. But still Dr. Stuhlinger waited. Finally he gave the signal. A radio message flashed up to the silently coasting rocket.

The flashes of the small upper stages could not be seen from the ground. But the instruments told that the rocket had burned properly. Now there was nothing to do but wait.

Scientists know that a rocket can go into an orbit which runs into the earth on the other side. The satellite has to go around the earth at least once before they can be sure it is in the right orbit. Meanwhile the time of firing was put on record. It was 11:48 P.M., January 31, 1958.

A New Jersey station first reported picking up the signals from Explorer. Nearly an hour later a California station reported that the signals had been picked up there. By that time Explorer had almost rounded the earth for the first time. It was high all around. It would not run into the earth.

All the reports were sent to Washington. From there it was announced: "Explorer is in orbit around the earth, making a complete trip in one hundred fifteen minutes. The first American-made satellite has been launched."

*Willy Ley*

# Universe

The Universe is all the skies
Reaching far beyond your eyes.

The Universe is all the seas
Spreading in unseen degrees.

The Universe is all the earth
Besides the spot that gave you birth.

If you can with your small eye
Know one star in all the sky:

If, of all the seas there be,
From one beach you know the sea:

If, of all the land on earth,
You can know one meadow's worth:

You might do a great deal worse
To understand the Universe.

*Eleanor Farjeon*

# Things to Think About and Do

1. Ask each member of your group to write a news story about one of the stories in this unit. Tell "Who," "When," "Where," and "What," in the first paragraph; then write other details. Make a page on the bulletin board to look like the front page of a newspaper, using the news stories. Write a weather report for one corner of the front page giving weather conditions in outer space.

2. Make an "Outer-Space Dictionary." List in *abc* order all the words you know that are needed in telling outer-space stories. Show how each word is pronounced, and give its meaning.

3. Explain each of these statements.

Walking was like standing in one place and letting the ground do the work.

The oxygen chills the tank and it becomes white with frost.

Bill was flying in complete silence.

"We'll seal ourselves in airtight. That'll help keep us light when we get into the atmosphere of Mars."

"It's because scientists daydreamed about space flight that we have satellites above us now."

The last words from the mountains of the moon came to them quite clearly, "Good-by. Good-by. Come back again!"

4. With members of your group set up an information center for a space-ship travel line. Make posters showing the planets to which the line carries passengers. Make a time table. Display books as suggested reading to prepare tourists for outer-space travel. Have a class member at the center to answer questions about planets, suggest clothing to take, and plan sight-seeing trips.

5. Rusty landed on the side of the moon that faces the earth. Pretend that you are to travel to the other side. What might you see there? What might you see as you looked out from the moon? Prepare a radio or television program to report your trip to your classroom listeners.

6. Which words below describe Glen in "Castaways in Space"? Which words remind you of another character? Who is it? Explain.

| alert | clever | nervous | skillful |
| fearful | gloomy | patient | generous |

7. Arrange these sentences from "Faster Than Sound" in the order of their happening.

The plane began to buck . . . like a wild horse.
Without power Bill started gliding downward.
Bill leveled off for his speed run.
Bill was heading straight for the sun.

# Some Books to Read

*Comets*, by Herbert Zim.

The author has written a history of comets from the earliest discoveries to modern times.

*Man-made Moons*, by Irving Adler.

Information on earth satellites and what they may be expected to do.

*Rusty's Space Ship*, by Evelyn S. Lampman.

The complete adventures of Rusty and Susan in their homemade space ship and what finally happened to them after they left the moon.

*Space Cat Meets Mars*, by Ruthven Todd.

Flyball, the cat, has a hair-raising adventure, when he travels to Mars.

*Starboy*, by Carl L. Biemiller.

Johnny Jenks meets the Man from Out There and his son, Remo, when they land in a flying saucer near his home.

*Wonderful Flight to the Mushroom Planet*, by Eleanor Cameron.

Two boys in a space ship dare dangers and have adventures that are out of this world.

*Danny Dunn and the Anti-gravity Paint*, by Jay Williams and Raymond Abrashkin.

The complete story of how the anti-gravity paint makes Danny's dream come true.

412

# In the Face
# of Danger

# Balto's Race against Death

With deeply serious eyes Dr. Curtis Welch looked around the hospital room. He knew that he faced a hard fight, alone, in the little town of Nome, Alaska, that cold winter of 1925.

Already three persons were dead.

Twenty-five more lay on the hospital beds, all ill with the same terrible disease—diphtheria. Only antitoxin could check the spread of the disease, and Dr. Welch had none. He must get some to Nome somehow. If the diphtheria were not checked now, it would spread like wildfire over the whole territory. Eleven thousand people were in great danger.

The hospital's one nurse came into the room, and the doctor moved toward the door. "Stay here until I return," he told her. "I am going to call the radio station."

A few minutes later the radio cry for help went flashing across the snows. Nome was near the Arctic Circle, many miles from the nearest railroad. It was frozen in by the sea. No ships could force their way through the thick ice. Yet those who heard the terrible news knew that help must be sent at once.

414

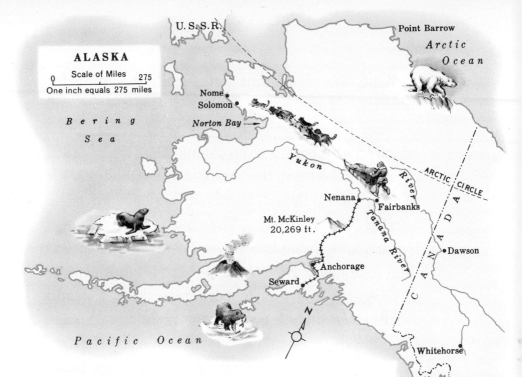

A doctor in southern Alaska was one of those who heard the cry for help. He had a good supply of antitoxin on hand, and early Tuesday morning wired, "Sending antitoxin to Nenana on today's train." The railroad went only as far as Nenana.

The precious twenty-pound package of antitoxin was started on its journey. After the three hundred miles by train, it would have to be carried six hundred and fifty miles over the snowbound trail stretching between Nenana and Nome.

Only dog teams could make it!

415

Again the radio sent out a call, this time for mushers. Mushers are drivers of dog teams, and one was chosen for each of the twenty relay posts which had been set up along the trail. Each musher picked out the strongest huskies from his kennel, and hitched them to a sled. Then he hurried to the trail. The hard trail between Nenana and Nome had never been covered in less than nine days. Now there were thousands of lives in danger. This was to be a race against death!

At eleven o'clock on Tuesday night the package of antitoxin was taken off the train at Nenana. The first musher was waiting with his dog team. He took the package and quickly set out on the trail. The great race was on!

416

It took until Saturday to cover the first four hundred fifty miles. The brave men who carried the antitoxin on this part of the long trail are remembered for their courage and endurance. However, special honor has been paid to the mushers who covered the last and most dangerous part of the journey.

On Saturday afternoon the package was given to Leonard Seppala. Seppala was one of the most daring mushers in the territory. He had come out from Nome to meet the antitoxin, covering almost two hundred miles of trail in four days.

Seppala hoped to carry the antitoxin all the way to Nome so that it would get there Sunday afternoon. This would mean returning to Nome in one day, in fresh-fallen snow and below-zero cold! With a rested team he turned back on the trail.

The team soon came to the edge of the ice-covered Norton Bay. Anxiously he stopped to look across the frozen water. It would be safer to take the land route, but that would add almost another hundred miles to the trip. Leonard Seppala made a quick choice. He would take the shorter, more dangerous way across the ice.

"Gee, Togo," he cried to his lead husky, and Togo headed his team over the ice of Norton Bay.

It was now dark, and Seppala was deeply concerned about the ice. Any minute it might break up and drift out to sea. Even Eskimos had been carried for miles on a drifting piece of ice before they knew it had broken loose. Some had been blown out into Bering Sea and drowned.

Togo picked his way carefully as the team raced along. Each husky seemed to know that Seppala was depending on him.

Midnight came. Seppala wondered if they were halfway across. How cold it was! What was the cracking noise? His heart stood still! Togo raced on as if he knew the danger.

418

At last the sky turned gray. The musher looked eagerly for signs of land. Ahead lay only an icy stretch. Or was that a shadowy coast line a bit to the right? A few minutes later he was sure. Another mile slipped by. They would make it safely—the ice would hold!

"Good dogs!" he cried proudly. "Gee, Togo!"

Togo led the team up the snowy bank. As they rounded a turn, Seppala saw a dog team and musher waiting on the trail. He would have liked to press on himself, but he knew it was wiser to let a fresh driver and team take over.

He stopped his sled beside the new team. "Here is the antitoxin," he said and handed over the package to Charlie Olson.

419

"Things are worse in Nome," Olson told Seppala. "Another death." His fingers were busy tying the package to his sled. "You made good time, Seppala."

Then Olson and his seven dogs were off. Twenty-five miles later, with his dogs almost frozen, Olson handed the antitoxin to Gunnar Kasson. It was eight o'clock Sunday night.

Gunnar Kasson, who lived in Nome, had been waiting in an empty cabin for two days and nights. With him were thirteen of the North's best huskies.

As he took the package from Olson he said, "I am going to take the antitoxin into the cabin for a few minutes. It may have frozen in the terrible wind."

The men waited inside the cabin for two hours, but the weather kept getting colder. It was now thirty below zero. Snow was beginning to fall. Kasson knew a snowstorm made dangerous going, but he said, "There is no use waiting any longer."

Stepping outside, he called his lead dog, "Hey, Balto!" The words seemed to be lost in the falling snow.

Thirteen balls of fur scrambled out of their warm snow nests at the sound of Kasson's voice.

420

"Here, Balto! Here, boy!"

A handsome husky, half-wolf, half-dog, ran to his place at the head of the team. As Kasson fastened the dog into his harness he said, "Tonight we'll have a hard pull, but I'm counting on you, Balto. We have to get through!"

The dog pricked up his ears and looked at his master as if he understood every word.

Kasson took his place on the sled. "Mush!" he cried.

The dogs headed out bravely on the crooked trail following the coast. It was hard pulling. Dogs and sled kept sinking into the heavy snow, but the team struggled on.

"I never felt a colder wind!" Kasson thought, trying to pull his long reindeer coat closer around him. Sealskin boots reached to his hips, and over these he wore sealskin clothing from head to foot, but the fierce eighty-mile polar wind whipped right through it.

The trail led straight into the wind. How could he or the dogs face it? He feared they would all be frozen to death. Even though they managed to keep going, how long could they stay on the trail?

He headed the team up a hill. Here there was nothing to stop the fury of the howling wind.

Next came a flat stretch six miles long. Would they ever get across it, with the wind whirling thick snow at them? Kasson was choked and blinded. He tried to catch sight of the dogs, but he could not see even the one nearest the sled. He was hopelessly lost. The antitoxin would never reach Nome.

Yet the sled kept moving steadily ahead. There was one hope left—that the dogs could keep the trail themselves. Kasson thought, "Balto will not fail me."

The great lead dog never stopped for a moment. Pushing ahead as fast as he could, Balto nosed out the trail on the wind-swept ice. For two hours Kasson held to the sled and trusted everything blindly to Balto.

They came to the tiny village of Solomon. Kasson could not even see the cabins, and passed right through the village. He didn't know that a message was waiting for him there. The message told him to stop in Solomon until the storm had cleared. Then he was to go on as far as Safety, where a fresh team and musher would take over.

423

Kasson sped on through the blizzard. If anything, the wind grew more bitter in the next twelve miles. When he at last came to Safety, the last of the relay posts, Kasson saw that the little town was dark. Not knowing that another musher was waiting, he raced past the village, and soon left Safety behind. Just twenty-one miles to Nome!

He was getting very tired. The dogs were slowing up, almost worn out. Deep drifts made the pulling terribly hard. Yet they struggled bravely on. They would reach Nome or die in their harness!

Suddenly Kasson felt the sled pitch roughly. The next second it tilted and he was thrown into the snow. As the sled overturned in a great drift, Balto slowed down and stopped the team. The dogs began to bark and fight.

424

Kasson jumped up and put the sled back on its runners. Then, lashing his whip, he quieted the dogs. It took him some time to straighten their harness in the dark. When they were ready to start again, he reached down to make sure that the antitoxin was safe. It was gone!

Crawling on his hands and knees, Kasson hunted wildly in the snow. The sled had turned over on its right side. Surely he would find the metal can there—if he had not lost it back on the trail! No, here it was! His heart began to beat again as he fastened the package tightly to the sled, with fingers that were stiff with cold.

As they set out once more the snowfall seemed lighter. At times Kasson could even see a bit of the trail ahead. Then in the dim light he noticed that two of the dogs were limping, overcome by the bitter cold. Stopping the team, he fastened a rabbitskin cover over each one, but he knew it wouldn't help much. The terrible cold could find a way through any cover. He told himself that if all his dogs died, he would still go on, carrying the package of antitoxin in his arms.

Now he was running behind the sled, for the team was swaying this way and that in a zigzag course. He wished for morning.

"Keep going, Balto," he cried. "We're almost there!"

Kasson peered ahead for a sight of the lumber mill on the edge of town. At last it appeared out of the falling snow. They had made it! The anti-toxin was in Nome! Brave mushers had brought it in five and a half days after the start at Nenana, traveling much of the time in a driving snowstorm.

Kasson's team seemed to know that the end of the great race was here. The dogs hurried past the mill, past a row of wooden houses. He heard people shouting, knew they were running after him. He turned the team to the left—there was the hospital! The crowd cheered as Dr. Welch took the package of antitoxin and shook his hand.

Half frozen and almost blinded Kasson dropped down into the snow beside Balto. "Balto!" he cried in a choked voice. "You did it! You brought us through! You brought us through!"

*Irma H. Taylor*

426

# The Wolf Cry

The Arctic moon hangs overhead;
   The wide white silence lies below.
A starveling pine stands lone and gaunt,
   Black-penciled on the snow.

Weird as the moan of sobbing winds,
   A lone, long call floats up from the trail;
And the naked soul of the frozen North
   Trembles in that wail.

*Lew Sarett*

427

# Two Chests of Treasure

Many years ago a boy lay asleep on a tiny island lost between the sky and water of the Caribbean Sea. Night was coming on. The boy wore fine clothes—velvet breeches, a linen shirt, and shoes with silver buckles. The shoes had the marks of salt water on them, and the fine linen shirt was dirty and ripped.

Suddenly the boy moved in his sleep. A sound had reached him over the water. It was the sound of a sail creaking in the wind. He leaped to his feet and ran to the edge of the rocks.

428

Yes, there was a ship, an English ship by the
build of her. She was standing off the island in
the dusk with the waves quietly lapping at her
hull. The boy drew in his breath for a shout,
then let it out again in a long, shivering sigh.
What he now saw was enough to frighten anyone.

A small boat was pulled up on the beach. Just
now two men were coming ashore from it. Each
man carried a heavy chest on his shoulder and
a spade in his hand. Behind them came a man
holding a ship's lantern. A pirate captain come to
bury his treasure! Even in the year 1680 such a
sight was enough to strike fear into any boy.

429

The three men came slowly up the beach.

"Here!" The captain pointed to a spot on the sand. "Dig a hole and be quick!"

The boy watched, hardly believing what he saw. This was no sailor's yarn, such as he had often heard on the docks at home. This was the real thing.

"Stop!" the captain said.

The men dropped their spades.

"Drop them in!"

The men lowered their burdens into the hole.

"Cover them up!"

The men threw sand onto the chests until they were covered. The captain watched them silently as the sand filled the hole.

As soon as the hole was filled and the men bent down to smooth the sand above it, the captain stepped close behind them. Two shots rang out, and the men fell forward. The boy watched with horror as the captain pocketed his pistols and picked up the lantern. Dead men tell no tales.

Still shivering with horror, the boy watched the captain climb the slope. At the top he stopped in his tracks and swung the lantern around his head as if he had gone crazy. Looking beyond him,

430

the boy saw the reason for the pirate's strange
actions. The ship that had been standing off the
island was now putting out to sea. It had left
its captain stranded on this desert island in the
Caribbean!

"Ahoy, sir!" the boy shouted. They now shared
the same danger. He thought that now he might
be safe with this cruel man. He knew that on this
tiny bit of land he could not long keep out of the
man's sight.

The captain whirled around and drew both his
pistols. "Who's that?" he cried.

"Don't shoot," called the boy. "I am stranded
on this island, just as you now are. I have a boat
with a sail. Shall we follow them?"

431

"We could never catch my ship. A fine lot they are!" He turned back to the sea and scowled fiercely at the departing ship. "But I've never given up yet. Who are ye, lad?"

"I'm Roger Wilkes from Port Royal," the boy answered.

"What are ye doing on this bit of rock?"

"I was shipwrecked and drifted eight days in a boat. I landed here today."

"Alone?"

"Yes, sir. When our ship went down, we were making ready the boats, but we were too late and all went down with her. When I came up, I saw a boat floating and climbed into it, but I never saw any of our crew again."

"Have ye any food or water?"

"A little," answered the boy, "and the mate had put his navigating instruments into the boat. I don't know how to use them, but perhaps you do."

"Yes, I can use navigating instruments," replied the captain. His eyes gleamed in the lantern light. "Show me the boat."

"She lies at the other side of the island," said Roger, and led the way to her.

The captain looked the little boat over carefully. Nothing in her escaped his sharp black eyes.

432

"She's fine," he said, "and these instruments are good. I could circle the world with them."

"Then we can get away from here," Roger cried. "It's lucky for us both."

"This all the water aboard?" The captain kicked a cask.

"Yes, and there's not a drop on the island. Let's start now."

"Easy, lad. We'll give the ship some time. If they sighted us at daylight they'd send us to the bottom to be rid of me."

"Did they turn against you, sir?" asked Roger.

"They didn't have the grit to do that," replied the captain, as he climbed out of the boat. He sat down on a rock and took off his hat. He smoothed the cherry-red plume with a careful hand. Then he looked up at the boy. "I suppose ye saw what happened tonight?"

Roger knew he spoke of the shooting. "I did," he said, "but bad luck has made us shipmates and closed my mouth."

The captain grinned. "Spoken like a gentleman," he said. "And dressed like a gentleman ye are too, in your velvet breeches. Your clothes are as fine as my own." And he smoothed the plume on his hat again as he spoke.

433

"My father was captain of a ship running between Port Royal and England," Roger told him. "She was a mail ship, the *Rose of Jamaica*."

"That was the ship that went down with ye aboard?" the captain asked. He seemed puzzled as he waited for Roger to answer.

"Oh, no. That was another ship. My father's ship has been missing a year past."

"Missing, ye say?"

"Yes, and it's strange that she should be missing. She was a good ship and had a full crew. There were no great storms at the time."

"Strange things happen at sea, lad."

434

"But I'll never believe what some people say happened." Roger spoke fiercely, and his eyes flashed with anger.

"To the *Rose of Jamaica?*" The captain fastened his eyes on the boy's face and seemed to wait eagerly for the answer.

"Yes, sir, to the *Rose of Jamaica.*" Roger was silent for a moment. Then he began to speak. "You see, she carried secret messages from the Governor of Jamaica to the King. Something about the Spanish. It is said that she sailed over to Spain and that my father sold the secret messages to the Spanish King."

"They say Captain Wilkes was a traitor?"

"So they say, but I know it isn't true. The crew must have turned against him and taken the ship to a port in Spain. They must have sold the messages, and they would have had to kill him first." Roger's voice dropped lower. "Still it is a

435

disgrace when a captain cannot handle his own crew. My father was a good captain. Something else must have happened, something which had nothing to do with the secret messages. My father was no traitor!"

The captain's voice broke in, and it was hard and cruel. "So! Ye think it a disgrace when a captain cannot handle his own crew. Do ye think I am in disgrace, then?"

Roger went cold as he listened to the captain's words. How could he have been so foolish? This man might kill him for what he had just said, but Roger would not back down now.

"I've said it, and I'll not take it back," he replied.

The captain laughed. It was a hard, cruel sound in the empty night.

"Ye have a brave tongue for a lad, and a brave heart. I like that, and for that I'll tell ye something. I may be in disgrace for being left here like a puppy, but the joke is on the crew. For many weeks now they've been muttering, and I know why. They smelled the treasure I had in my cabin. My own treasure it was, too, my fair share of the hauls we had made."

"They wanted it?"

436

"That they did. They'd spent their own, and they wanted mine. So I hid it under my cabin floor, right in front of the door. I was a ship's carpenter once, and I did a good carpenter's job. Then I filled two chests with sand and came ashore here as if to bury my treasure. Yes, lad, those chests are full of sand and that's a fact." He threw back his head and laughed.

"But you have lost your treasure," Roger pointed out. "Your crew has your ship."

"I'll find it again. I'll find my ship, for I know this old Spanish Main as you know your good right hand."

"Then let's be going. The wind is right. Your ship will be far out of sight by morning, and we'll be safe from it."

For a full minute the captain gazed at the stars. Then he said, "Is everything aboard?"

"Everything," Roger answered eagerly.

By the light of the lantern the captain looked carefully at the oars, the sail, everything.

The captain got into the boat. "Push her out," he said to Roger. "I'll steer with an oar past that point of rock."

Roger pushed the boat until the water came up to his chest. Then he started to climb aboard.

437

"Stand off!" The captain's voice cut like a knife.

The boy looked past the lantern, which was on a boat seat, and saw a pistol pointed at his head.

"What are you doing?" His voice was high with fear, and he sank back in the water.

"It's me or you," the captain said, "and having the upper hand, it's me that gets away."

"You're going to leave me here!"

"That's right. One cask of water's not enough for two. I'll leave ye here or shoot ye where ye stand. It'll help none to whimper."

"I'm not whimpering!" The boy's eyes looked fiercely back at the pirate captain. "I'll not whimper for anyone as cruel and selfish as you."

438

"Lad," the captain said in a voice that was a bit less hard, "I've liked your spirit from the start. I'd take ye if I could, but it would be the death of both of us."

"I gave you all I had. I trusted you—you pirate!"

"I'm a man as wants to live. Ye may be took off the island by a passing ship."

"You know a ship never comes near this island—not once in a moon."

"Maybe, but I'll give ye a little news to comfort ye while ye wait. It was I that sent the *Rose of Jamaica* to the bottom."

"You killed my father!"

"He died fighting like a man."

"Thank you for that—if it is true."

"It's true. We needed supplies, so when we sighted a ship, we ran up signals calling for help. When she came over to us and lowered her sails, we climbed aboard and took her."

Roger was too full of hate and sadness to say anything. The captain went on talking.

"Listen, lad. I took the captain's papers, thinking they might come in handy. Many a time I've saved my skin by knowing what was in a ship's papers. Among these was the secret

439

messages ye spoke of. I kept them, for it's things like that as saves a man's neck sometimes. They're in my cabin now, and when I get back my ship— and I *will* get her back—I'll send those papers to the Governor of Jamaica with a word that'll clear up your father's name. That'll pay for this boat I'm taking. Now, will ye go ashore?"

Roger went ashore. Slowly the captain rowed away from land, then raised the sail and disappeared in the darkness.

There was nothing to do now but bury the two dead men, and this Roger did. Then he dug up the chests. The captain had told the truth. They were filled with sand!

By the second morning Roger's thirst was bothering him. Hour by hour it grew harder to bear. He prayed for a storm, but no storm came. The next day hunger gnawed at his stomach and he could hardly draw breath past his swollen tongue.

He didn't know when a ship sailed quietly toward the island and dropped her anchor offshore. Night had come, but even in the darkness the sailors knew this coast, for they had been here once before. This was the pirate ship coming back for the chests of treasure her captain had buried here a few days ago.

440

At sunrise a small boat put out from the ship and came to shore. Almost at once the pirates saw a figure lying on the rocks. This was the captain now dead of thirst, they thought, and they laughed at their revenge.

The sailor who reached him first let out a cry. "This is a lad!"

"Then where's the old man?"

"Search the island."

Shouts soon rang out when one of the sailors found the chests as Roger had left them. Eagerly they lifted the lids.

"Full of sand!" They stood in a ring and stared.

"The lad knows something about this!"

"He's dead."

"No, he's not," the mate said. "Ye'll take him aboard, and ye'll care for him like he was your own mother's son. He's the only one who can give us the treasure."

There was sense in that, and they saw it, so they carried Roger to the ship and cared for him until he had his sea legs under him once more.

One day, with the deck of the old pirate ship rolling under his feet, he said to the mate, "It was all done for treasure. The thought makes me sick."

"Where is the treasure?" the mate asked. The other pirates drew close, listening for the answer.

"I know where it is," said Roger.

"We'll give ye a share," promised the mate.

"You will not." The boy shivered as if a cold wind had hit him. "It's blood money a thousand times over. I want none of it."

"Ye'd best tell us where it is." A muttering began in the group of pirates standing around the boy, but Roger had not lost the courage that had struck into the cruel heart of the captain.

"I'll bargain with you first. In the captain's cabin on this ship are papers taken from the *Rose of Jamaica*. When you set me ashore in Jamaica,

442

with those papers in my possession, I will tell you where the treasure is. I give you my word that every bit of it shall be yours. Kill me here, and I vow you will lose it all."

He looked into the fierce eyes about him. He knew he had the upper hand. They knew it too. There were threats, but at last on a dark night he was rowed ashore at a point where the mountains of Jamaica meet the sea. There he kept his bargain and told the mate the secret of the treasure, of how it lay under the cabin floor. Then he turned and ran toward the town where the lights of home twinkled peacefully.

*Merritt P. Allen*

# The Feather of the Northman

Donald MacDermott was on his way to Fort
Vancouver. For days he and a group of trappers
had been traveling down the Columbia River in
a fleet of canoes. Through swift and smoothly
flowing water, over rapids and around whirlpools,
they had glided along the great waterway.

It was Donald's first trip to the fort. His father,
Big Mac, had died only a little while ago. Now
Young Mac, as he was called, was traveling west
to seek his fortune.

444

He was under the protection of his father's old friend, Henri Le Grand. Henri had made up his mind that this thirteen-year-old boy should grow up to be a man Big Mac could be proud of. He had seen to it that Donald shared every hardship on this trip, which in the year 1832 had been full of hardship.

Many times they had had to leave the Columbia to make a portage over the rough trails with their canoes and their supplies. Every night a fire had to be kept burning to frighten away wild animals, and the food was wormy and bad.

445

Donald, though he was homesick and afraid, did not want any of the men to know how he felt. He had taken every hardship without whimpering. Even the teasing of these woodsmen, he had taken in his stride, or at least had tried to, but he had not returned their joking. And as the miles increased between him and his home, he had grown more sullen and quiet.

The men might lift their voices in loud song as they drove their canoes through the water, but not Donald. He sat silent and unhappy. When they joked, he set his mouth firmly and did not smile, and so the men had made him the target of their fooling.

The teasing had increased each day until Donald wondered how he could stand another hour of it, but still he held his tongue and his songs and smiles.

Now they were within one day's traveling of the fort. Tomorrow the fleet of canoes would reach Fort Vancouver. Tomorrow he and the others would jump to land before the canoes had touched the shore. Tomorrow he was going to sing with the rest of them.

But deep in his heart there would be no singing, because Donald knew what the others didn't

446

know. He knew that he was secretly afraid of this wilderness. That fear was the reason he was sullen and homesick. It was the reason he could not laugh and sing.

Donald lay wrapped in his warm blanket and watched the hazy white moon climb high above the towering rocks that lined the opposite bank of the river. Lying there, he fought his fear until, worn out with weariness, he dropped asleep.

He was awakened by a low snarl, which he recognized, even before he was fully awake, as the snarl of a timber wolf. His hand closed quickly on his gun, which lay on the ground beside him. He lifted his head cautiously and peered about.

He listened, hardly breathing. Had he only dreamed that threatening snarl?

It had seemed to come from near at hand. But now there was not a sound to be heard, other than the usual out-of-door sounds—the hoot of an owl, the stir of wind in the branches, the soft lap of water against the river bank. The camp lay quiet and peaceful in the moonlight.

The bed of coals left from the campfire drew his eyes. Those bulky heaps on the ground beyond the fire must be Baptiste, the cook, and Jacques, under their blankets, their feet toward the fire.

447

In chill weather the men all slept close to the fires, but this night air was pleasant, and the trappers lay scattered around the camp. Some were in the open, and some under the shelter of their upturned canoes.

The boy was surprised to see that no one was on guard duty. Did they believe this country so safe, then?

Donald looked around for Henri. He was relieved to see his friend only a few yards away, lying like a big bundle in his Hudson's Bay blanket. Henri never slept under a canoe unless it was storming. He didn't want walls of any kind around him when he was on the march.

448

It was a means of self-protection he had learned in dangerous Indian country long ago. No matter how sharp a man's eyes might be, Henri said, they couldn't see through wood. Too, Henri slept with his ears wide open. He would have been awakened the very first thing if any enemy, human or animal, had been moving around the camp. That snarl must have been only part of a dream.

Donald's tight grip on the rifle loosened. He was about to settle back into his warm blanket, when a movement near his feet jerked him once more into sharp attention.

In a nearby upturned canoe his eyes made out the shadowy shape of a large animal. It was a snarling timber wolf, its fangs bared, ready to pounce.

The boy felt a chill, like a cold hand, run along his backbone. He stopped for just a second while the chill shook him. Then he snatched his rifle, but before he could fire, the animal fell on its side.

449

Donald lowered his rifle and stared. The fallen animal didn't move. It appeared to be dead, though no shot had been fired. Cautiously the surprised boy drew himself to a sitting position and gently reached out and pushed the quiet figure with the barrel of his rifle. The figure did not move.

Then a smothered laugh from behind the canoe made Donald suddenly understand. The animal was dead! Its lifeless body had been propped up there as a joke on him!

Donald leaped over the body of the wolf and peered behind the canoe. Sure enough, there were Jacques and Baptiste, shaking with smothered laughter.

"Shhh!" whispered Jacques, his finger on his lip. "Make no noise to wake that wolf, Young Mac! She is one big, bad, evil wolf, *non*?"

"Ho, little brother!" gasped Baptiste. "What are you doing out with your gun at midnight? Not hunting, surely?"

Suddenly the whole camp seemed to be laughing at him. The boy turned to see figures rising from the ground all over the camp. Then he knew that the men had not been asleep at all, but were waiting to see how the joke on him turned out.

450

At first a wave of anger swept over Donald, but it passed as quickly as it had come. He had a proud feeling. They had all seen that he was not timid, that he was not a coward!

To be awakened from a sound sleep to find a snarling wolf at one's bedside—that was enough to frighten any man, surely! He had felt fear, to be sure, but he had thrown it off. Let them have their fun! They had seen that he was no coward. If he had covered his head and called for help— but no one could say that he had shown fear.

Resting one end of his rifle on the ground, the boy folded his arms across his chest, put one foot on the dead wolf, and faced the laughing camp with an air of triumph.

"Behold!" he cried in French. "Behold a real hunter!"

The men fell silent to listen.

"You call yourselves hunters!" Donald called out. "You boast of your fine shots! Many times I have heard you tell how you killed a bear with only one shot. One shot, bah! *You* have to *shoot* to kill! Young Mac has only to raise his gun, and the wild animals fall dead from fright! You have just seen it happen!"

Henri's powerful shoulders shook with laughter. Good enough! Young Mac was boasting now in the true trapper style.

A roar of cheers went up from the men. The boy had turned the tables on them nicely, and they were not only willing, but delighted, to admit his victory. Young Mac was truly one of them— at last. He would have a tall tale of his own to tell now. They clapped one another on the back and shouted, "Ha! So you thought you were a hunter, eh? But you have to shoot to kill! Bah!"

Henri Le Grand quieted their cheers with an upheld hand. The guide went toward Donald, and the men came near and made a half circle around the two. The boy's eyes widened. His heart began to beat quickly, for he saw that Henri held in his hand a band of plaid ribbon with a red feather fastened to it. It was the plaid of the MacDermott clan. The men were perfectly quiet now, watching their guide and Young Mac.

"Tomorrow," said Henri Le Grand, "Young Mac's first voyage will end at Fort Vancouver. A long, hard journey it was, and he did his share all the way. He took his place at the paddle with the best of you. Whenever there was need, he carried his heavy pack like a man. He ate what he was offered without a grumble. When there was nothing in the pots for supper, he pulled his belt tighter and said not a word, though all his growing bones cried out for food. He sat tight when the canoes shot rapids. Not even at the Canyon of the Dead, where the tall white crosses tell of boatmen who died in the boiling water, did he show fear. Did any of you see him show fear?"

"*Non! Non!*"

"Now you have just seen him frighten a timber wolf to death. Is he not one of us? Is Young Mac not a Northman?"

"*Oui! Oui!*" the trappers shouted. "Yes! Yes! He is one of us. Behold Young Mac, the Northman!"

453

"You have learned the law of the trapper," Henri said to Donald, "the law that has made the sons of the fur trade able to look death in the face without blinking. You have learned well that law: to know fear, as all men must know fear, but not to be conquered by fear; to think clearly and quickly; to keep a high heart. It is decided that you have earned the right to wear the feather of a Northman."

Henri lifted his arms to place the band on Donald's head, a ribbon with the plaid of Big Mac's clan and a red feather.

"So tall the boy has grown!" the man thought. It seemed to him only yesterday that he had swung this lad up to ride on his shoulder along with his own son.

"Now then! It is done!" He pressed the headpiece in place. "Have you not something to say, Young Mac?"

"*Merci!*" said Donald almost in a whisper. He felt that he could not speak above the pounding of his heart.

"Oho!" laughed Henri. "Say more, Young Mac, and speak the language of England, not France! That is the language they use at Fort Vancouver!"

Donald turned toward the watching men and saluted them with dignity. He spoke in the language that he had not used for some time, not since Big Mac had spoken it with him.

"Thank you. I—I am very proud that you call me one of you. Thank you all. I shall keep forever the red feather to remind me that I am a Northman. And—some day we will go on another voyage—together."

The night air rang with the hurrahs of the trappers. While the cheering was still going on, Jacques and Baptiste climbed up a tree as quickly as squirrels.

"But, you two! Where are you going?" Henri shouted after them.

"We go to cut a lobstick!" Jacques shouted back.

Baptiste's voice called, as branches showered from the tree, "Yes! We mark forever the spot where Young Mac, a real hunter, saved his brothers from the fierce, evil wolf!" In trapper style the story was already growing tall!

"A lobstick for Young Mac, of course!" the men agreed, several of them leaping to join the two at work in the tree. And before long they had slashed a tree clean of its branches except for a little bunch at the very top. It would be a sign to all who came this way that something important in trapper history had happened on this spot.

Long after the quiet of sleep had settled down on the camp, Young Mac lay awake. He had something precious to keep forever now—the Northman feather, a reward for his courage. Yes, and this night he had won another victory, something that would allow him to wear that feather proudly. It was an understanding that had come to him with Henri's words: "To know fear, as all men must know fear, but not to be conquered by fear."

He understood now that it was not unmanly to feel fear and to be lonely. It was unmanly only to let fear and loneliness conquer one.

The great men of the fur trade, even the strongest, had known fear. They, too, had been sick at heart sometimes, in the lonely wilderness where they had to spend months—years—of their lives. Maybe they, too, at times had felt that it would be easier to weep than to laugh.

His own father? Suddenly, with a clearness that startled him, Donald remembered something from his childhood.

He had run in out of the snow, where he and a friend had been trying to teach Bairn to pull a sled, when Bairn was still a puppy and didn't want to learn such serious business. Donald had run into the house for a piece of harness, and had been surprised to see his father sitting there with his face in his hands. He had asked, "Are you asleep, Father?"

His father had looked up with a strange smile and had said something strange.

"Not asleep! I was just remembering—"

The words had small meaning for Donald then, and, as it happens in childhood, he forgot them right away. Now, when they came back across the years, he understood. His father, far from his home, had been lonely, remembering.

The boy put up his hand and touched the precious headpiece above him, which hung from the canoe. He marked the date well in his mind— October 18, 1832. He would not forget this day when the men had decided that he had earned the right to wear the Northman feather. He knew now that he could meet whatever hardships lay ahead with a brave heart. Tomorrow—Fort Vancouver—let them come!

*Mary Jane Carr*

# Forest Boat Song

The dawn is comin', callin',
Canoemen must away;
The road is long before us,
And hot the summer day.
Oh, dip the cedar paddles deep,
We must hasten on our way.

The road is long before us,
And hot the summer day;
The storm may break upon us,
The rapids cause delay.
Oh, dip the cedar paddles deep,
We must hasten on our way.

But voyageurs undaunted,
We do not know dismay,
The portage trail is waitin',
And camp, at end of day.
Oh, dip the cedar paddles deep,
We must hasten on our way.

*Richard Clyde Ford*

459

# Hoosier Barbecue

Bud and his father were on their way to the barbecue. It was much too hot for comfort. There had been no rain in southern Indiana for several weeks. All about them stood the tall corn. The road was like a narrow canyon between two high, dusty green walls, which shut out all but a narrow blue river of the sky.

They drove about five miles through the unchanging cornland, until the road ended suddenly on a bluff overlooking the Wabash River. Bud's father whistled as he jammed on the brakes, and the car stopped about ten feet from the edge.

"Boy!" he said.

Bud looked down over the bluff and caught his breath. The river was fifty feet or more below them. Far away he saw a few white cranes, and an empty barge on the river. Suddenly he thought he was going to smother in the noon heat. There wasn't enough breeze even to rattle the cornstalks.

"Why did they ever build a road right to the edge like this?" he asked.

"They didn't," his father said. "In the spring the river flooded and bit off a piece of the land. That's why the corn grows right to the edge of the bluff too. The land caved into the river after the corn was planted—maybe five or ten acres of it. We'd better back out of here!"

So they backed and tried another fork in the dusty road, and then another and another, until finally they struck a gravel road.

"Well, this is more like it!" Bud's father said.

Very soon they were climbing a low, round hill that rose like an island in the sea of cornland— a little island of green grass and cottonwood trees.

"Here we are!" Bud's father said, and they parked the car among the others that were already there. They climbed out, stretching their legs.

"Well, well! If it isn't Bud and his pa!"

461

It was Bud's grandpa, who was picking his way toward them among the cars.

Bud liked his grandpa. He liked the way he was always hitching up the faded blue shoulder straps of his overalls. He liked the scrubbed, brown gleam of his grandpa's cheeks, that was like the gleam of new leather.

"We got lost," Bud said.

"Lost, eh?" Grandpa laughed. "Well, I'm not a bit surprised! Not a bit! They tell me there are city fellows wandering around in these river bottoms today that came down ten years ago just to shoot a few ducks!"

He laughed again, then suddenly grew serious. With a sweep of his arm he took in the countryside and began to talk as if he were with a group of strangers, instead of his own son and grandson.

"This is in the heart of the bottoms where the Wabash and Ohio rivers meet. There's a good gravel road all the way down here, but I guess you missed it. When the Ohio is at flood stage this land is under water. In the big flood of '37 the water came right up over the top of this hill."

"Really!" said Bud.

"Yes, sir! This is an Indian mound, you see. It isn't natural. It was made hundreds of years ago

462

by the Mound Builders. They buried their dead in it. It's an Indian grave.

"Why, Bud, your pa and his brothers used to find bones, flint arrowheads, and clay cooking pots here when they were kids. They say you don't have to dig down more than a foot or two."

He stopped as if he were thinking over what he had just said. Then he looked up quickly and said, "But what am I doing, standing here talking when you two must be half-starved? Come on! Let's get going to the barbecue. It's right over there on that other mound. This one's just for parking cars."

463

As they started down into the hollow between the two mounds, he gave Bud's hair a tug.

"Good old hickory barbecue, Bud! Beef, mutton, or pork! You can take your pick, or a big helping of each. There's plenty of barbecue sauce, tomato catsup, or anything you want to go with it."

Bud felt his stomach grow emptier, and he hurried down through the hollow at a run.

As they crossed a creek halfway to the second Indian mound, the scent of the hickory smoke reached Bud's nose. The picnickers were all gathered. All the farmers and farmers' wives in the country seemed to be on top of the hill, eating and laughing and talking.

Bud made straight for the barbecue pit and held out his plate to the man who was carving and serving. "Some beef and some pork," he said, and the man heaped his plate with the juicy meat.

By the time Bud was through eating, the crowd was moving away from the barbecue pit and the tables to the speakers' stand. There the Governor of Indiana was waiting to give his speech.

Bud had already decided he didn't want to listen to speeches. Something else was filling his mind—his grandpa's words, "You only have to dig down a foot or two! An Indian mound—bones—flint arrowheads—cooking pots!"

He ran down into the hollow without being seen by anyone and crossed the creek to the mound where the cars were parked.

465

There was an old shed on the mound, and in it Bud found what he wanted—a spade. He hung around for several minutes in the shed, looking at a rowboat and some fishing gear stored there. Then he went out and began to dig.

The earth was dry and hard and dusty. Though he worked in the shade, he was very hot and bugs swarmed 'round his head. He dug and dug, making ditches and pits and shallow holes, but all he found was a piece of rotten harness strap, a rusty chisel, and a dog's bone.

"Arrowheads and cooking pots, like fun," he growled. "Grandpa was only joking."

Because he was busy with his work, Bud did not see the change coming into the sky. So when the first drop of rain fell, it startled him. It was a huge drop that splashed down beside him like

466

a ball of lead. It made a brown circle in the dust as big as a half dollar. After it came another— and then another and another. One struck the back of his neck and felt like ice.

Bud looked up. The sky was an angry yellow and growing darker. The wind was whipping the boughs of the cottonwoods. The air was so hot and heavy that everything wilted before it, and it choked him, like dust. The cranes were gone.

For one moment Bud gazed across the hollow at the picnic grounds, wondering if he should run for it and join his father and grandpa. The rain decided for him. It came all at once, dumped on him, not in drops but in pailfuls, from the darkening sky. Along with it came a crash of thunder. He brushed his soaked hair out of his eyes and ran blindly toward the shed through the almost solid wall of water.

"It's a cloudburst!" he gasped, shaking himself when he was inside the shed. "It's a real cloudburst—like the one we had last summer!"

He sat down in the stern of the rowboat. The sagging roof above him could not hold out against the force of the storm, and in a few minutes rain was leaking through upon him in little showers. Bud did not care. He liked it.

The rain lasted twenty minutes. Then, as suddenly as it had started, it stopped, leaving only the drip of water from the roof and the trickle of little streams all about.

Bud stepped out of the shed and looked around. The air was fresh and clean. The dust had been washed from the grass and the cottonwoods, and the world was painted a new green. In the parking lot the cars sparkled brightly where the sun reached them.

"Oh, boy!" Bud said to himself. "I'll bet the barbecue got soaked!" He walked around the shed to look across the hollow and was stopped short.

The hollow was gone. Between him and the picnic ground he saw, instead, a wide stretch of brown water. He stood still with his mouth open, staring. He could not believe that the quiet little creek could have grown to a small river in less than half an hour.

But it had, and there on the picnic ground the people were staring helplessly at the yellow-brown flood, just as he was.

Suddenly it came to him how helpless they were. From his own Indian mound the road was still above water and all right. But from their Indian mound there was no road. They were no

468

longer on a mound. They were on an island, with no means of escape. Bud's eyes widened. His mouth fell open a little farther.

"Wow!" he said aloud. "They're marooned!"

Then he began to yell.

"Hello! Dad! Grandpa! Hello!"

When at last they saw him, they began to yell too, but he could not understand what they were saying. He could only see them jumping up and down, waving their arms. Even the Governor was waving.

At last Bud realized it was hopeless. They could not understand each other. He would have to go and get help. He turned and walked back around the shed.

It was then that fear hit him for the first time, right in the middle of his stomach. He remembered the bottom lands which he and his father had ridden over earlier in the day, the tall corn, the winding roads, and the awful loneliness. If he left his Indian mound and went down into the bottom lands to search for help, he would surely get lost. He would never find his way.

He began to shiver, his wet shirt cold now on his back, his mind suddenly filled with a hundred crowding fears. It would be growing dark in a few hours. He could not reach his father, and his father could not reach him. He would have to spend the night alone on a mound where the Mound Builders used to bury their dead.

It was all he could do to keep from crying. Luckily at that second his eyes fell on the gleaming rowboat in the shed. At once his mind became clear and his fears disappeared. He would row across the flooded hollow.

It was no easy job dragging the rowboat out across the rain-soaked earth—pulling and pushing. Once on the water, the rowing was the hardest he had ever done. Whirlpools and currents steadily tugged the bow, so half the time he seemed to be rowing in the wrong direction.

Bud was not a Hoosier boy for nothing. He was at home in a rowboat. He knew the tricks of flood currents and whirlpools. His arms were strong and brown and hard. When he was halfway across, he had the applause of the marooned picnickers to spur him on.

Still, it seemed to take forever to get across the stretch of water. His arms ached. His hands hurt. His head grew dizzy. The meat and cake he had eaten were like chunks of lead in his stomach.

But at last he made it.

In the excitement that followed his landing, the people almost overlooked him. They patted him on the head, of course, and a half-dozen women called him a hero, but the farmers were feeling worried about the Governor, who was soaked to the skin and none too happy about it. So they set to work at once rowing him and his party across to the mound where the cars were parked.

After the Governor was taken care of, the rescue work went ahead quickly. Some of the men went home and brought back their own boats to put into service. At last all the picnickers were safely ferried across the swollen creek and on their way home.

Bud and his father crossed on the last trip with Grandpa. By the time they reached the parking lot and climbed into their car, Bud was dead tired. His arms and legs ached. His eyes were heavy. He wished Grandpa would finish repeating his directions and let them start home. Then Grandpa said something that made him sit up straight.

"And now, Bud, I want to tell you how proud I am of you. You did a dangerous thing bringing that boat across the flood—and a brave thing. You acted like a man!"

*William E. Wilson*

472

# Things to Think About and Do

1. Draw a picture for each story in this unit. Write a date and a title under each picture. Join the pictures to make a time line for the unit.

2. What might you hear as you read each of these sentences? What might you feel?

All about them stood the tall corn.
Kasson sped on through the blizzard.
The picnickers were all gathered on the Mound.
Henri slept under a canoe when it was storming.
A ship sailed quietly toward the island.
They slashed a tree clean of its branches.
Then, lashing his whip, he quieted the dogs.
"Full of sand!" They stood in a ring and stared.

3. Which person faced the worst hardships in the stories in this unit? Copy the list of hardships below and grade them from the worst hardship to the least hardship. Give reasons for your grading.

Roger was shipwrecked and landed on an island.
Rain leaked through upon Bud in little showers.
Donald didn't complain when the food was wormy.
An eighty-mile wind tore through Kasson's clothing.
Donald had to carry supplies over rough trails.

4. What is the difference between a hardship and a danger? Which character faced the worst dangers?

5. List the ways dogs have helped man through the ages. Two suggestions are given below.

to herd sheep          in rescue work

6. Get information about huskies from the encyclopedia and other books. Make a list of points that make them suited for work in the Arctic Circle. Compare them with other dogs for such work. Report your findings to the group. Use pictures to prove some of your points.

7. Match the words in the first column with those in the second column. Use each pair of matching words in a sentence.

| | |
|---|---|
| Ohio River | Arctic Circle |
| Fort Vancouver | Mound Builders |
| Caribbean Sea | Wabash River |
| Indiana | Jamaica |
| Nome | Columbia River |

8. Use a mimeographed copy or draw a large map of the world. List under each continent below the names of the stories in *Trails to Treasure* which took place on that continent.

North America    South America    Europe

Plan to draw or cut out a symbol for each story. Draw or paste the symbol on the map to show the part of the continent where the story took place.
474

# Some Books to Read

*Capture at Sea*, by Audrey Beyer.

A story of the War of 1812. Two boys who are seized from a merchant vessel experience a battle at sea.

*The Horse without a Head*, by Paul Berna.

A group of boys and girls in a French town outwit a gang of train robbers.

*The Long Winter*, by Laura Ingalls Wilder.

A brave family faces a long, hard winter on the plains in pioneer days.

*The Ordeal of the Young Hunter*, by Jonreed Lauritzen.

A Navaho boy's concern for his father's sheep sets him on a trail of danger.

*Sudden Voyage*, by Vera R. Amrein.

Unexpected dangers were lying in wait for Nora, Mark, and Toby when they sailed their sloop on Long Island Sound.

*Sybil Ludington's Ride*, by Erick Berry.

Sybil was a courageous girl who met with adventure during Revolutionary War days.

*Pirate's Promise*, by Clyde Robert Bulla.

Tom was on his way to America when his ship was captured by pirates.

# Glossary

This glossary will help you to pronounce and to understand the meanings of the more difficult words in this book. A number after a definition tells you the first page on which the word, or some form of the word, is used with that particular meaning.

Below is a list of pronunciation symbols and of words that tell you the sounds for which the symbols stand. It is called a pronunciation key.

| | | | | | |
|---|---|---|---|---|---|
| ā | lāte | ī | hīde | ū | ūse |
| å | al'wåys | ĭ | hĭd | u̇ | u̇ nite' |
| ă | ăm | ĭ | pos'sĭ ble | ŭ | ŭs |
| ă | ăp pear' | | | ŭ | cir'cŭs |
| ä | färm | ō | ōld | û | bûrn |
| ȧ | ȧsk | ȯ | ȯ bey' | | |
| a | a lone' | ŏ | nŏt | o͞o | mo͞on |
| â | câre | ǒ | cǒn trol' | o͝o | fo͝ot |
| | | ô | hôrse | oi | oil |
| ē | wē | o̩ | so̩ft. | ou | out |
| e̩ | e̩ nough' | | | t̶h̶ | t̶h̶at |
| ĕ | wĕt | | | th | thin |
| ě | si'lěnt | | | | |
| ẽ | let'tẽr | | | | |

## A

**ab bre'vi a'tion** (ă brē'vĭ ā'shŭn). A short form of a word or phrase. (83)

**Ad ji dau'mo** (ă jĭ dô'mō). Indian word for *squirrel*. (348)

**ad just'** (ă jŭst'). 1. To move the parts of an instrument or machine so that they fit together in working order. (145) 2: To fit; as to *adjust* oneself to a new school.

**ae'on** (ē'ŏn). A very long period of time, not fixed as to number of years; an age of the world or universe. (150)

**Al'ex an'der** (ăl'ĕg zăn'dẽr) (356–323 B.C.) A king who conquered most of the world of his time. (310)

**A lois'** (ȧ lois'). The main character in a tale of Switzerland. (109)

**an'cient** (ān'shĕnt). Belonging to times long past. (106)

**An'dro cles** (ăn'drŏ klēz). The name of a Roman slave of the first century A.D. (317)

**an'ti con'tact rub'ber** (ăn'tĭ kŏn'tăkt rŭb'ẽr). A substance of a kind that does not stick or cling. (384)

476

**an'ti tox'in** (ăn'tĭ tŏk'sĭn). A substance formed in the blood of a person who is sick with a germ disease. It helps to overcome the disease. A like substance in the blood of animals is used in treating human beings. (414)

**an'vil** (ăn'vĭl). A metal block on which hot met- al is pounded to change its shape. (153)

Anvil.

**ap pease'** (ă pēz'). To make calm; to quiet by satisfying demands; as, to *appease* one's hunger. (107)

**ap plause'** (ă plôz'). Clapping one's hands or cheering to show pleasure or approval. (351)

**ap pre'ci a'tion** (ă prē'shĭ ā'shŭn). 1. The valuing of a person or thing at its true worth. (91) 2. Being grateful for something; as, to show *appreciation* for a gift. 3. Intelligent enjoyment; as, an *appreciation* of music.

**ap pren'tice** (ă prĕn'tĭs). A person learning a trade or craft under a skilled worker; a beginner. (156)

**arc** (ärk). A part of a curved line, as of a circle. (405)

**arch'bish'op** (ärch'bĭsh'ŭp). The bishop of highest rank in a group of districts. (164)

**arch'er y** (är'chĕr ĭ). Shooting with bows and arrows. (340)

**a re'na** (ȧ rē'nȧ). 1. In ancient Rome, a place where gladiators fought and other public contests and displays took place. (319)

2. A space where public contests or shows take place.

**ar'mor plate** (är'mēr plāt). Metal sheets or plates used for protection, as on a battleship. (359)

**as sign'ment** (ă sīn'mĕnt). 1. A job to be done. (362) 2. The act of giving a person a duty to perform or a place to go.

**as tron'o my** (ăs trŏn'ŏ mē). The science that deals with heavenly bodies. (140)

**at'mos phere** (ăt'mŏs fēr). 1. The layer of gases around a planet. (364) 2. The air of a particular place; as, a stuffy *atmosphere* in a room.

**A'tri** (ā'trē). A district, or part, of Italy. (321)

**at tempt'** (ă tĕmpt'). To try; to make an effort. (161)

**Aus'tri a** (ôs'trĭ ȧ). A country in Central Europe. (163)

**ax'is** (ăk'sĭs). A straight line, real or imaginary, which passes through a body and on which the body turns. (95)

## B

**Bairn** (bârn). A dog in "The Feather of the Northman." (458)

**Bal'to** (bôl'tō). A brave husky. (414)

**Bap tiste'** (bȧ tēst'). The name of a French cook. (447)

**bar'be cue** (bär'bĕ kū). 1. A gathering of many persons out of doors for a feast of *barbecued* meat and for entertainment. (460) 2. To roast an animal whole or in large pieces over an open fire. 3. To cook meat or fish in a highly seasoned sauce.

**Ba'sel** (bä'zĕl). A city in Switzerland. (109)

**be guile'** (bĕ gīl'). To cause time to pass in a pleasant way; to amuse. (106)

**Ben gal'** (bĕn gôl'). A province, or part, of India. **Bengal Tiger.** A large, short-haired, striped animal of the cat family. (86)

**boul'der** (bōl'dĕr). A large rounded stone or mass of rock. (22)

**bow'er** (bou'ẽr). A shelter of leafy branches or vines; an arbor. (263)

**brack'en** (brăk'ĕn). A large, coarse fern, or group of such ferns. (263)

Bracken.

**bran'dish** (brăn'dĭsh). To wave or shake in a threatening way. (296)

**Braun, Wern'her von** (brôn, wẽr'nẽr vôn). A specialist in rocket design, the building of liquid-fuel rockets, and rocket-power plants for guided missiles. (399)

**buck'thorn'** (bŭk'thôrn'). A tree or bush, often with thorny branches. (188)

**Bun'yan, Paul.** See **Paul Bunyan**

**buoy** (boō'ĭ or boi). A floating object anchored in a body of water to show where

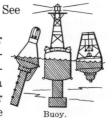
Buoy.

a rock or reef is, or to mark a channel. (46)

478

**butte** (būt). A steep hill or small mountain, standing alone. (188)

## C

**cac'tus** (kăk'tŭs). Plants with fleshy stems and with scales or spines instead of leaves. Cacti can grow in hot, dry regions. (220)

Cactus.

**ca det'** (kȧ dĕt'). A young man who is in a school training for the army, navy, or air force. (382)

**ca nal'** (kȧ năl'). 1. Faint, narrow markings on the planet Mars that appear at certain times of the year. (391) 2. An artificial waterway for boats or for irrigation.

**Cape Ca nav'er al** (kāp kȧ năv'ẽr ăl). A cape on the east coast of Florida. (399)

**cap'sule** (kăp'sūl). A small container in which something is enclosed, such as a medicine, so that it may be swallowed easily. (387)

**car'a van** (kăr'ȧ văn). A group of people, traveling together through a desert or through dangerous country. (252)

**car'bu ret'or** (kär'bŭ rā'tẽr). The part of a motor or engine in which liquid fuel, such as gasoline, is mixed with air to make it explosive. (66)

**ca ress'** (kȧ rĕs'). An act or expression of affection. (87)

**Car'ib be'an** (kăr'ĭ bē'ăn). The part of the Atlantic Ocean between the West Indies and Central and South America. (428)

cast'a way' (kȧst'ȧ wā'). A person who has been stranded; cast adrift. (382)

cas'u al (kăzh' u̇ ȧl). 1. Careless; free of worry. (19) 2. Happening by chance; as, a *casual* meeting.

cav'al cade' (kăv'ȧl kād'). A parade especially of persons on horseback. (171)

cha me'le on (kȧ mē'lē ŭn). A kind of small lizard that is able to change the color of its skin. (87)

cham'ois (shăm'ĭ).

1. A goatlike antelope that lives among the mountain peaks of Europe and Asia. (117) 2. A soft leather.

Chamois.

Char bon neau' (shȧr bô nō'). The husband of Sacajawea, the Indian woman who guided Lewis and Clark. (288)

chas tise' (chăs tīz'). To punish; especially, to punish bodily, as by whipping. (108)

Chi'ca (chē'kȧ). The name of a horse in a western story. (23)

Chi nook' (shĭ no͞ok'). 1. A kind of salmon. (10) 2. An American Indian of Oregon and Washington. 3. (*not cap.*) A moist southwest wind that blows over the coast of Oregon and Washington. 4. (*not cap.*) A warm dry wind that descends the Rocky Mountains.

chro nom'e ter (krō nŏm'ē tẽr). An instrument for measuring time. (141)

cin'na mon (sĭn'ȧ mŭn). 1. A spice made from the bark of certain trees. (264) 2. Color of *cinnamon*.

cit'i zen (sĭt'ĭ zĕn). 1. A person who lives in a city or town. (67) 2. A person who owes allegiance to a government and who has a right to protection from it.

clan (klăn). A group of families who have a common forefather; as a great-grandfather. (453)

cod (kŏd). A deep-water food fish found in the colder parts of the North Atlantic Ocean. (226)

cog (kŏg). A tooth on the rim of a wheel in a machine or other tools or instruments. (95)

Co lum'bi a (kȯ lŭm'bĭ ȧ). A large river in British Columbia and the states of Washington and Oregon. (444)

com'et (kŏm'ĕt). A bright heavenly body, usually having a long, cloudy tail, that moves around the sun. (148)

com pos'er (kŏm pōz'er). A person who composes, or puts something together; especially, a person who writes music. (168)

com'po si'tion (kŏm'pȯ zĭsh'ŭn). 1. Something formed by putting together; as, a piece of music or writing. (189) 2. The material

---

lāte, alwȧys, ăm, ȧppear, färm, ȧsk, ȧlone, câre, wē, ĕnough, wĕt, silĕnt, lettẽr, hīde, hĭd, possĭble, ōld, ȯbey, nŏt, cȯntrol, hôrse, sŏft, ūse, ūnite, ŭs, circŭs, bûrn, mo͞on, fo͝ot, oil, out, that, thin

or substance of which something is made up or composed.

**con'cert** (kŏn'sûrt). A musical performance at which several persons sing or play instruments, or do both. (165)

**Con'gress** (kŏng'grĕs). The national lawmaking body of the United States, consisting of the Senate and the House of Representatives. (88)

**con'quer** (kŏng'kẽr). To overcome; to get the better of. (132)

**cor ral'** (kŏ răl'). A pen for keeping or capturing animals. (34)

**crafts'man** (krȧfts'măn). A skilled workman. (171)

**cra'ter** (krā'tẽr). The bowl-shaped hole around the mouth of a volcano. (365)

Crater.

**Crock'ett, Da'vy** (krŏk'ĕt, dā'vĭ). An American pioneer. (88)

**cross'bow'** (krŏs'bō'). A weapon used in olden times for shooting arrows or stones. It had a bow set crosswise on a handle. (329)

**cruise** (kro͞oz). To travel by ship or aircraft from place to place, without going directly to any one place. (394)

**Cu'ba** (kū'bȧ). A large island in the West Indies. (134)

**D**

**dain'ty** (dān'tĭ). Delicate and pretty. (309)

**de flect'** (dĕ flĕkt'). To turn aside; to change the direction of. (359)

**de gree'** (dĕ grē'). 1. A mark, as on a thermometer, that shows the amount of something, such as heat or cold. (396) 2. A step in a series; as, to advance by *degrees.*

**dem'on stra'tion** (dĕm'ŭn strā'shŭn). 1. Showing something new or how something works. (80) 2. A display of feeling; as, a *demonstration* of joy.

**de spise'** (dĕ spīz'). To have a strong dislike for; to look down upon with scorn. (316)

**de ter'mined** (dĕ tûr'mĭnd). 1. Decided; having one's mind firmly made up. (129)

**De troit'** (dĕ troit'). A city in the southeastern part of Michigan. (152)

**dia'blo** (dyä'blō). 1. A Spanish word meaning devil. 2. Tara's burro. (216)

**diph the'ri a** (dĭf thĕr'ĭ ȧ). A contagious disease which affects the throat. (414)

**dis cern'** (dĭ zûrn'). To make out by the eye or mind; to recognize; to see. (86)

**dis guise'** (dĭs gīz'). 1. Clothing put on to keep secret who one really is. (304)

**dis'trict** (dĭs'trĭkt). A part of a place, such as a town or state, marked out for a special purpose. (36)

**Doug'las** (dŭg'lȧs). 1. A timber tree of great size of the western United States. (238) 2. The name of a company that builds aircraft. (394)

**duch'ess** (dŭch'ĕs). The wife or widow of a duke; also, a woman who has a rank equal to that of a duke. (167)

**dy'na mite** (dī'nȧ mīt). 1. An explosive used in blasting. (104) 2. To blow up with dynamite.

## E

**Ear'hart, A mel'ia** (âr'härt, ȧ mēl'yȧ). A famous woman flyer. (126)

**eaves** (ēvz). The lower overhanging edge of a roof. (281)

Eaves.

**Ed'i son, Thom'as** (ĕd'ĭ sŭn, tŏm'-ȧs). A famous American inventor. (85)

**ef fect'** (ĕ fĕkt'). Something that is produced by a cause; result. (364)

**e lec'tron'ic** (ĕ lĕk'trŏn'ĭk). The science that deals with such things as vacuum tubes, radar, radio, and television. (387)

**El Ran'cho** (ĕl răn'chō). The name of a Mexican hacienda. (215)

**e mer'gen cy** (ĕ mûr'jĕn sĭ). An unexpected happening that calls for prompt action. (198)

**em ploy'** (ĕm ploi'). To hire; to use the services of. (157)

**en dur'ance** (ĕn dūr'ȧns). The ability to hold out or keep on. (60)

**en'ter prise** (ĕn'tĕr prīz). 1. An undertaking; a project. (161) 2. Willingness to undertake difficult projects.

**E o'pee** (ĕ ō'pē). An imaginary planet. (366)

**Ep'i me'theus** (ĕp'ĭ mē'thūs). The husband of Pandora, in a Greek myth. (302)

**e qua'tor** (ĕ kwā'tĕr). An imaginary circle around the earth, halfway between the North Pole and the South Pole. (131)

**e quip'ment** (ĕ kwĭp'mĕnt). Supplies needed for a special purpose, as for a camping trip. (358)

**es pe'cial ly** (ĕs pĕsh'ȧl ĭ). Unusually; extra; also, chiefly. (257)

**Eu'clid** (ū'klĭd). 1. The name of a science professor in a story. (374) 2. A famous Greek teacher of geometry.

**Eu'rope** (ū'rŭp). A continent east of the Atlantic Ocean and west of Asia. (149)

**e'vil** (ē'v'l). 1. Harmful; hurtful. (308) 2. Bad; wicked; as, an *evil* deed.

**ex ult'** (ĕg zŭlt'). To feel joy; to be in high spirits. (351)

## F

**fa'ble** (fā'b'l). 1. A story that teaches a lesson, especially one in which animals act like people. (352) 2. A story that is not true.

lāte, alwãys, ăm, ȧppear, färm, ȧsk, ȧlone, câre, wē, ĕnough, wĕt, silĕnt, lettĕr, hīde, hĭd, possĭble, ōld, ȯbey, nŏt, cŏntrol, hôrse, sŏft, ūse, ūnite, ŭs, circŭs, bûrn, mōōn, fŏŏt, oil, out, that, thin

**fath'om** (făth'ŭm). A measure of length equal to six feet, used chiefly in measuring depth of water. (226)

**Fin'lay, Car'los** (fĭn'lȧ, kär'lōs). A Cuban-American doctor. (133)

**fore'cas tle** (fōk's'l or fōr'kȧs'l). The forward part of a vessel where the crew sleeps. (232)

**forge** (fôrj). 1. A furnace, or a place with a furnace, where metal is heated and hammered into shape. (153) 2. To heat and hammer metal into shape.

**for sooth'** (fŏr sŏŏth'). Indeed; certainly. (316)

**Fort Van cou'ver** (fōrt văn kŏŏ'vĕr). A former trading post and fort on the Columbia River. It was about one hundred miles from the mouth of the river. (444)

**fra'grant** (frā'grȧnt). Sweet in smell. (223)

**fran'ti cal ly** (frăn'tĭk lĭ). Excitedly; wildly. (270)

**fu'ture** (fū'tŭr). Time coming after the present; what is to come. (109)

## G

**gal'ley** (găl'ĭ). 1. The kitchen of a ship. (224) 2. A large, low ship used in olden times, usually propelled by oars.

**gaunt** (gônt). Very thin and bony. (106)

**gen'er al** (jĕn'ĕr ȧl). 1. Taken as a whole; not in small parts. (292) 2. An army officer of the highest rank.

**gen'ius** (jēn'yŭs). 1. A very gifted person. (61) 2. Great natural ability.

**Gess'ler** (gĕs'lĕr). A cruel ruler of Switzerland at the time of William Tell. (328)

**gla'cier** (glā'shĕr). A large mass of ice that moves slowly down a slope or across a large area. (161)

**glimpse** (glĭmps). 1. To catch a brief view of. (31) 2. A very quick look; a glance.

**Glouces'ter** (glŏs'tĕr). A city on the coast of Massachusetts. It is famous for its fishing fleet. (224)

**Grand Ba ha'ma** (grănd bȧ hä'mȧ). One of the Bahama Islands in the West Indies. (400)

**grav'i ty** (grăv'ĭ tĭ). The force that causes objects to move toward the center of the earth. (367)

**Gre'cian** (grē'shȧn). Greek. (106)

**grim** (grĭm). 1. In a determined way. (83) 2. Stern; also, fierce.

## H

**hac'i en'da** (hȧs'ĭ ĕn'dȧ). A Spanish-American word meaning a large ranch or large estate; also, a country house. (214)

**harp'si chord** (härp'sĭ kôrd). A wire-stringed, harp-shaped musical instrument having a keyboard. It was in use before the piano. (164)

**hatch** (hăch). An opening in the deck of a ship; the covering for such an opening. (231)

**heave** (hēv). 1. To lift or raise, usually with an effort. (227) 2. To throw; as, to *heave* a rock.

herald                                    **Kasson**

**her'ald** (hĕr'ăld). 1. In
olden times, an of-
ficer who made an-
nouncements. (342)
2. To give news of;
to announce.

**Hi'a wa'tha** (hī'å wô'-
thå). The Indian
hero of a poem by
Longfellow. (348)      Herald.

**Hin'du** (hĭn'dōō). A member of a
native race of
India. (107)

**ho'gan** (hō'gôn).
An earth-cov-
ered dwelling
of the Navaho
Indians. (223)      Hogan.

**Hoo'sier** (hōō'zhĕr). 1. In or belonging to the state of Indiana. (460)
2. A citizen of Indiana.

**ho ri'zon** (hŏ rī'z'n). The line where
the earth and sky, or sea and
sky, seem to meet. (397)

## I

**I a'goo** (ē ä'gōō). The name of the
great boaster in the poem, "Hiawatha's Hunting." (348)

**im plore'** (ĭm plōr'). To beg; to
plead. (46)

**in fect'** (in fĕkt'). To poison with
something that causes disease,
such as germs, bacteria, or virus.
(138)

**in'stant** (ĭn'stănt). Closely following
in time; immediate. (332)

**in'stru ment** (ĭn'strŏŏ mĕnt). 1. A
tool; a mechanical device. (141)
2. A device by which musical
sounds are made. (168)

**in tel'li gence** (ĭn tĕl'ĭ jĕns). Understanding; ability to learn and
know. (119)

**Ir'by** (ẽr'bĭ). The main character
in a story laid in the southern
mountains. (199)

**Ire'land** (īr'lănd). One of the British
Isles. (130)

**It'a ly** (ĭt'å lĭ). A country in southern Europe. (323)

## J

**Jacques** (zhåk). The name of a
French trapper. (447)

**ja lop'y** (jå lŏp'ĭ). An automobile or
airplane in a partly worn-out
condition. (205)

**Ja mai'ca** (jå mā'kå). An island in
the West Indies. (434)

**Ja-Nez'** (jä nĕz'). The name of a
Navaho boy's burro. (223)

**Jo sé'** (hŏ sā'). A Mexican worker
.on the hacienda *El Rancho*. (215)

**ju'bi lee** (jōō'bĭ lē). A state of joy;
shouts of joy. (251)

**Ju'pi ter** (jōō'pĭ tẽr). 1. A planet.
(371) 2. The name of a type of
rocket. (399)

## K

**Kas'son, Gun'nar** (käs'sôn, gŭn'når).
The name of a brave musher.
(420)

---

lāte, alwåys, ăm, ăppear, färm, åsk, ȧlone, câre, wē, ĕnough, wĕt, silĕnt, lettẽr,
hīde, hĭd, possĭble, ōld, ȯbey, nŏt, cŏntrol, hôrse, sŏft, ūse, ûnite, ŭs, circŭs, bûrn,
mōōn, fŏŏt, oil, out, that, thin

**483**

**knowl'edge** (nŏl'ĕj). Learning; understanding. (149)

## L

**lair** (lâr). Bed of a wild animal. (237)

**law'yer** (lô'yẽr). A person who knows or practices law. (170)

**La zear', Jes'se** (là zēr', jĕs'ĕ). An army doctor with Walter Reed in Cuba. (135)

**league** (lēg). A group of persons, teams, or nations for carrying out some common purpose. (43)

**leg'end** (lĕj'ĕnd). 1. A title or a brief description beneath an illustration. (172) 2. An old story that is widely accepted as true but cannot be proved to be so. (352)

**Le Grand', Henri'** (lē grän', än rē'). The name of a French guide. (445)

**Lew'is, Mer'i weth er** (lū'ĭs, mĕr'ĭ-wĕth ẽr). An American explorer. (287)

**Lu ci'o** (lōō chē'ō). The name of Tara's understanding uncle. (210)

**lunge** (lŭnj). A sudden plunging forward; a leap. (14)

**lurch** (lûrch). A sudden roll of a ship to one side; also, a staggering movement to one side. (382)

## M

**Mac Der'mott, Don'ald** (măk dẽr'-mŏt, dŏn'ăld). A boy who traveled to Fort Vancouver with French trappers. (444)

484

**Mac'e do'ni a** (măs'ĕ dō'nĭ à). An ancient country in Europe, north of Greece. (310)

**Mahn-go-tay'see** (män gō tā'sē). An Indian name for Hiawatha. (351)

**maj'es ty** (măj'ĕs tĭ). 1. Royal dignity; stateliness. (150) 2. A person who has power of government. (168)

**Man'dan** (măn'dăn). 1. A tribe of Plains Indians. (287) 2. A city in North Dakota.

**man'i fold** (măn'ĭ fōld). Great, both in number and kind; many and varied. (171)

**man'za ni'ta** (măn'zà nē'tà). A kind of shrub of the western part of the United States. (180)

**Ma'rie' An'toi'nette'** (mà'rē' än'twà'-nĕt'). She became the wife of Louis XVI of France. (167)

**mar'ma lade** (mär'mà lād). A kind of thick, pulpy jam. (106)

**ma roon'** (mà rōōn'). To put a person ashore on a lonely coast or on an island and leave him alone. (469)

**mass  pro duc'tion** (măs  prŏ dŭk-shŭn). Goods produced in great numbers, usually by machinery. (160)

**mel'o dy** (mĕl'ŏ dĭ). A tune; sweet music. (106)

**mer'chant** (mûr'chănt). A person who buys and sells; a trader. (170)

**mer ci'** (mĕr sē'). French word for *thanks*. (455)

**me'sa** (mā'sȧ). A flat-topped hill having steep sides. Such hills are common in the Southwest. (177)

Mesa.

**Mi am'i** (mī ăm'ĭ). A city in the southern part of Florida. (131)

**mir'a cle** (mĭr'ȧ k'l). A wonderful happening that cannot be explained by any known law of nature. (116)

**mi'ser** (mī'zĕr). A grasping, mean person; especially, a person who lives in a poor manner in order to save money and keep it. (324)

**Mis'e re're** (mĭz'ĕ rā'rĕ). A musical setting of one of the psalms. (169)

**mis'sile** (mĭs'ĭl). A weapon or other object designed to be thrown or shot. (399)

**mis'sion** (mĭsh'ŭn). 1. A task given to a plane or group of planes. (358) 2. A group of missionaries; also, a place where missionaries live and work. 3. A person's life work.

**Mitch'ell, Ma ri'a** (mĭch'ĕl, mȧ rī'ȧ). A famous astronomer. (140)

**mor'al** (mŏr'ăl). 1. The inner meaning of, or a lesson to be learned from, a story or an experience. (316) 2. Of good character.

**Mo ran', John J.** (mŏ răn', jŏn). An American soldier with Walter Reed in Cuba. (138)

**Morse code** (môrs kōd). The alphabet used to send messages by telegraph. It is made up of dots, dashes, and spaces. (191)

**Mt. Ev'er est** (mount ĕv'ĕr ĕst). A mountain of the Himalayas, the highest mountain in the world. (55)

**Mo'zart, Wolf'gang** (mō tsärt, vôlf'gäng). A famous composer of music. (163, 164)

**mus'cle** (mŭs''l). An organ of the body which produces motion; also, the tissue of which such an organ is made. (277)

**myr'i ad** (mĭr'ĭ ăd). A very great number. (150)

**myth** (mĭth). 1. A legendary story used to describe some fact of nature or to explain a religious belief or practice; as, the *myths* of ancient Greece. (352) 2. A person or thing that exists only in one's imagination.

## N

**Nan tuck'et** (năn tŭk'ĕt). A large island off the coast of Massachusetts. (140)

**nav'i gate** (năv'ĭ gāt). The science

---

lāte, alwȧys, ăm, ȧppear, färm, ȧsk, ȧlone, câre, wē, ènough, wĕt, silĕnt, lettēr, hīde, hĭd, possĭble, ōld, ŏbey, nŏt, cŏntrol, hôrse, sŏft, ūse, ûnite, ŭs, circŭs, bûrn, mōōn, fŏŏt, oil, out, that, thin

of figuring out the course of a ship or an airplane, and steering it in the right direction. (432)

**Ne nan'a** (nĕ năn'ȧ). A city in the east-central part of Alaska. (415)

**New Guin'ea** (nū gĭn'ĭ). A large island north of Australia. (131)

**no'ble** (nō'b'l). 1. Having great dignity. (86) 2. Great in goodness or uprightness; as, a *noble* man.

**No ko'mis** (nȯ kō'mĭs). Hiawatha's grandmother and nurse. (348)

**non'plus** (nŏn'plŭs). To puzzle or perplex; to bewilder. (87)

**Noon'an, Fred** (nōō'năn, frĕd). An airplane pilot. (131)

**nov'ice** (nŏv'ĭs). A person who is new at something; a beginner. (87)

**O**

**On tar'i o** (ŏn târ'ĭ ō). A province of Canada. (190)

**op'er a'tor** (ŏp'ĕr ā'tĕr). A person who runs, or operates, something, such as a machine. (194)

**or'ches tra** (ôr'kĕs trȧ). A group of players on various musical instruments, especially stringed instruments. (164)

**oui** (wē). French word for *yes*. (453)

**P**

**Pa'lo mi'no** (pă'lȯ mē'nō). 1. The name of a valley in a story laid in southern California. (176) 2. A breed of horses.

**pal'pi tate** (păl'pĭ tāt). To beat fast and hard; to throb; also, to flutter. (350)

486

**Pan do'ra** (păn dō'rȧ). A beautiful woman told about in a Greek myth. (302)

**pan'ther** (păn'-thĕr). A large and fierce wild-cat. (89)

Panther.

**Paul Bun'yan** (pôl bŭn'yăn). A giant lumberjack, hero of many legends told in American lumber camps. (97)

**Paw nee'** (pô nē'). A member of an important Indian tribe, now citizens of Oklahoma. (285)

**peas'ant** (pĕz'ănt). In countries of Europe, a tiller of the soil, either as the owner of a small farm or as a farm hand. (117)

**pen'ance** (pĕn'ăns). An act to show sorrow for wrongdoing. (46)

**per'i scope** (pĕr'ĭ skōp). An instrument consisting of a tube equipped with mirrors so that a person looking through one end can see objects in range of the other end. (357)

**pe'so** (pā'sō). A coin of some Spanish-speaking countries, as Mexico, Cuba, the Philippines, etc. (212)

**Pho'bos** (fō'bŭs). The inner satellite of Mars. (384)

**Pierre** (pyâr). The French name of a boy who lived in the province of Ontario. (189)

**pi'ñon** (pē'nyōn or pĭn'yŭn). A low-growing pine of Mexico and southwestern United States. (180)

**Plac'er ville** (plăs'ĕr vĭl). A town in California. The discovery of gold made Placerville one of the richest towns in California in the 1850's. (264)

**plague** (plāg). 1. Anything that causes trouble; *in common use*, a nuisance. (47) 2. A very dangerous contagious disease. 3. To tease.

**plaid** (plăd). A pattern in cloth, having narrow bands of different colors crossing one another. (453)

**por'tage** (pōr'tĭj). The carrying of boats or goods overland from one body of water to another, or around falls and rapids. (445)

**pres'sure** (prĕsh'ẽr). A pressing, or bearing down upon. (157)

**prey** (prā). 1. An animal hunted or killed by another animal for food. 2. To hunt, seize, or pounce upon. **beasts of prey.** Animals that feed upon the flesh of other animals. (87)

**pro test'** (prŏ tĕst'). 1. To object to; as, to *protest* a decision in a ball game. (220) 2. To declare in a positive way; to state. (267)

**Puer'to Ri'co** (pwĕr'tō rē'kō). An island of the West Indies. (400)

**pul'ley** (pŏŏl'ĭ).

A wheel with a grooved rim in which a rope or chain runs, used in lifting, or in running a machine. (104)

Pulley.

**py'thon** (pī'thŏn). A large snake that crushes its prey. It is found in India and Malay countries. (108)

Python.

## R

**ra'di a'tor** (rā'dĭ ā'tẽr). A device used to heat air, as in a room, or to cool an object, such as an automobile engine. (64)

**rav'en ous** (răv'ĕn ŭs). Very hungry; greedy. (106)

**re'al ize** (rē'ăl īz). 1. To understand; to grasp the facts. (291) 2. To accomplish; as, to *realize* one's ambition.

**rec'og nize** (rĕk'ŏg nīz). 1. To remember knowing; to know again. (202) 2. To make some sign to show one knows a person, as to nod or wave.

**rec'ord** (rĕk'ẽrd). 1. The best that has ever been done, as in a contest. (129) 2. The known facts about something, as about a person's life. 3. A disk on which sounds are reproduced for use on a record player.

**re ward'** (rē wôrd'). 1. To make a suitable return for something; to repay. (293) 2. Something given in return for some service or deed well done.

**roe'buck'** (rō'bŭk'). A kind of deer. (348)

---

lāte, alwãys, ăm, ȧppear, färm, ȧsk, ȧlone, câre, wē, ĕnough, wĕt, silĕnt, lettẽr, hīde, hĭd, possĭble, ōld, ōbey, nŏt, cŏntrol, hôrse, sŏft, ūse, ūnite, ŭs, circŭs, bûrn, mōōn, fŏŏt, oil, out, that, thin

# S

**Sac a ja we'a** (săk *à* jà wē'*à*). A young Indian woman who guided Lewis and Clark. (286)

**salm'on** (săm'*ŭ*n). A large food fish with pinkish or reddish flesh. (10)

**Salz'burg** (sôlz'bûrg). An important city in Austria. (163)

**sat'el lite** (săt'*ĕ* līt). In astronomy, a smaller body that revolves around a larger body. (375)

**Sat'urn** (săt'ẽrn). The large planet that is encircled by rings. (360)

**schol'ar** (skŏl'ẽr). A person who knows a great deal about one or more subjects. (112)

**schoon'er** (skōōn'ẽr). A sailing vessel with two or more masts and with its sails rigged in a line with the sides of the vessel. (224)

**scull** (skŭl). To move a boat by working an oar in a twisting motion over the stern of the boat. (237)

**sem'a phore** (sĕm'*à* fōr). A device for giving signals from a distance by means of lights, moving arms, or flags. (195)

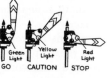

Semaphores.

**se ñor'** (sä nyôr'). A Spanish word meaning *Mr.* or *sir*; also, a gentleman. (218)

**Sep pa'la, Leon'ard** (sä pä'l*à*, lĕn'ẽrd). A daring Alaskan musher. (417)

**serv'ice** (sûr'vĭs). 1. Help; to do good to. (139) 2. Performance of duty; work.

**sex'tant** (sĕks'tănt). An instrument for measuring distances, used especially at sea to observe heights in order to determine latitude and longitude. (144)

**Sho sho'ne** (shŏ shō'nĕ). An Indian tribe of the Northwest. (286)

**si es'ta** (sĭ ĕs'tà). A nap or rest, especially one at midday. (214)

**Sin'ga pore'** (sĭng'gà pōr'). An important seaport on an island off southeastern Asia. (46)

**Sioux** (sōō). A tribe of Indians of the Great Plains. (296)

**Soan-ge-ta'ha** (sōn gĕ tä'hä). The Indian word for Strong-Heart; a name given Hiawatha. (351)

**Sol'o mon** (sŏl'ŏ mŭn). A village in Alaska. (423)

**som bre'ro** (sŏm brä'rō). A hat with a broad brim worn in Spanish America and in the southwestern United States. (215)

**sound'ing lead** (sound'ĭng lĕd). A weight at the end of a line used to measure depth; a sounding line. (226)

Sounding lead.

**sour'dough'** (sour'dō'). A prospector of Canada or Alaska, so called from the habit of carrying sour dough, a fermented dough used in making bread. (102)

**stal'lion** (stăl'yŭn). A male horse. (311)

**starve'ling** (stärv'lĭng). A person, animal, or plant that is very thin from lack of food or nourishment. (427)

**stead′fast** (stĕd′fȧst). Not changing; firm; steady. (295)

**stir′rup** (stĭr′ŭp). A loop hung by a strap from a saddle and used in pairs to support the feet of a person on horseback. (26)

**strad′dle** (străd″l). To stand, sit, or walk with the legs spread wide apart; also, to spread out in an irregular way. (27)

**Stuh′ling er, Ernst** (stoo′lĭng gẽr, ûrnst). One of the scientists working on rockets at Cape Canaveral. (406)

**Stultz** (stoolts). An airplane pilot with Amelia Earhart. (128)

**suc ceed′** (sŭk sēd′). To do well; to have success. (157)

**sug ges′tion** (sŭg jĕs′chŭn). 1. Bringing to mind; the act of suggesting. (123) 2. Something suggested.

**sul′len** (sŭl′ĕn). Silent in a gloomy way. (446)

**Swiss** (swĭs). 1. Of or having to do with Switzerland. (328) 2. One who is a citizen of Switzerland.

**Switz′er land** (swĭt′zẽr lănd). A small, mountainous country in central Europe. (328)

### T

**tal′ent** (tăl′ĕnt). Natural ability; especially, a gift for doing some particular thing very well. (165)

**Ta′ra** (tä′rȧ). The name of a Tarascan Indian boy. (210)

**Ta ras′can** (tä räs′kăn). An important tribe of Mexican Indians. (210)

**taw′ny** (tô′nĭ). A yellowish-brown color. (86)

**tel′e graph** (tĕl′ĕ grȧf). 1. An electric device for sending messages by code. (194) 2. To send a message by *telegraph*.

**ten′dril** (tĕn′drĭl). A slender, leafless stem on a climbing plant which twists around something for support. (323)

**the′o ry** (thē′ŏ rĭ). An opinion or explanation about something, based on observation and reason. A theory may or may not be true. (134)

**till′er** (tĭl′ẽr).
1. A handle used to turn the rudder of a boat in order to steer it. (290) 2. A person who tills the soil; a farmer.

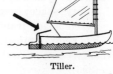

Tiller.

**tin′der** (tĭn′dẽr). Something that catches fire easily; especially, material used to catch fire from a spark. (94)

**Tiph′i a** (tĭf′ĭ ȧ). The name of an outer-space character. (362)

**to′paz** (tō′păz). A stone, that is classed as a gem, usually orange-yellow in color; also, the color of such a stone. (150)

**tor til′la** (tôr tē′yä). A thin, flat cake, usually of corn meal, baked on a heated stone or iron. (213)

---

lāte, alwȧys, ăm, ȧppear, färm, ȧsk, ȧlone, câre, wē, ĕnough, wĕt, silĕnt, lettẽr, hīde, hĭd, possĭble, ōld, ōbey, nŏt, cŏntrol, hôrse, sŏft, ūse, ûnite, ŭs, circŭs, bûrn, moon, foot, oil, out, that, thin

**tract** (trăkt). An area or region not definitely bounded. (286)

**trai'tor** (trā'tēr). A person who is not true to or is false to; as, a *traitor* to one's country. (435)

**tri'umph** (trī'ŭmf). 1. Joy because of victory or success. (147) 2. To gain a victory.

## U

**un daunt'ed** (ŭn dôn'tĕd). Fearless; brave. (459)

**urge** (ûrj). 1. To force to go faster. (27) 2. To plead for.

## V

**vac'u um** (văk'û ŭm). A perfectly empty space; especially, an enclosed space from which the air has been pumped. (383)

**vaunt** (vônt). To boast; to brag. (296)

**vent** (vĕnt). 1. A hole or opening for air, gas, or smoke. (403) 2. To give expression to; as, to *vent* one's anger.

**vex** (vĕks). To make impatient or cross; to anger. (150)

**Vi en'na** (vĕ ĕn'á). The capital city of Austria. (166)

**vi'rus** (vī'rŭs). The poisonous substance that contains the germs of a disease. (137)

**vol'un teer'** (vŏl'ŭn tēr'). A person who of his own free will offers himself for some service. (136)

**Von Braun, Wern'her.** See **Braun, Wernher von.**

## W

**Wa'bash** (wô'băsh). A river in Indiana and Ohio that flows into the Ohio River. (460)

**wa'fer** (wā'fēr). 1. A very thin, crisp cake or biscuit. (115) 2. A very thin piece of candy.

**war'ri or** (wŏr'ĭ ēr). A fighting man; a soldier. (310)

**weird** (wērd). Unnatural; ghostly; wild. (380)

**wit'ness** (wĭt'nĕs). 1. A person who is present when something happens; as, a *witness* of an accident. (150) 2. A person who gives testimony in court.

## Y

**yon'der** (yŏn'dēr). Over there; at that place. (311)

**Yu'ca tan'** (yōō'ká tăn'). A state and peninsula in southeastern Mexico. (108)

490

# To the Teacher

This Fifth Reader, *Trails to Treasure*, follows *Roads to Everywhere*, the Fourth Reader of the GINN BASIC READING SERIES.

This Fifth Reader introduces 1012 new words. Except for a few pages of poetry, no more than six new words appear on any page.

Words on this list that appear in the glossary are starred. Foreign words and poetry words that are not repeated are italicized. These words are not included in the word count.

## New Words in This Book

**UNIT I**

10 Huggins
salmon*
Chinook*
Grumbie
11 Ribsy
worst
Scooter
McCarthy
brag
12 beach
jellyfish
13 scales
tackle
14 movement
scoop
soaked
gritted
lunge*
dripping
15 flung
gills
16 miserably
waded
flop
17 plodded
18 spun
19 camera
casual*
20 tough

21 thunder
22 staggering
stumbling
*crumbling*

*boulder**
dazzle
distant
haze

23 Chica*
mysterious
24 meant
jog
Nutmeg
Muley
mare
25 bones
26 catalogue
pretend
swell
stirrup*
27 straddling*
urged*
canter
glowing
Zeb
brains
28 . . .
29 scrambled
zigzagged
30 tossing
31 sped
glimpse*
bored
32 filed
33 streaked
porcupine
34 twigs
pride
twice

corral*

35 Chuck
Clifford
Bronco
diamond
36 district*
No.
Orioles
37 stubbornly
bother
shrill
excuse
38 Welch
39 foul
40 single
bunt
41 . . .
42 center
admit
control
43 split
league*
Jojo
Smith
44 nerve
45 ramp
catsup

46 Godfrey
Gordon
Gustavus
Gore
doubt
implore*

wrung
tore
deaf
*buoy**
*Nore*
folks
oar
threatened
voyage
*penance**
Singapore*
47 mercy
*plague**

48 stripes
Barbara
hedge
skunk
49 glands
50 . . .
51 mistake
plume
vet's
52 . . .
53 arguing
54 risked
television
model
55 Tensing
Mt. Everest*
peaks
56 dining
57 . . .
58 . . .
59 . . .

60 Adele
  Treadway
  drank
  Ott
  Lincoln
  Link
  endurance*
61 sports
  state
  genius*
  Harmony
62 nation's
  mechanic
  celebration
  event
  polished
  enter
63 brass
64 charge
  Dr.
  crank
  radiator*
65 mad
  rammed
66 slight
  Fords
  carburetor*
  patched
  junk
67 citizens*
  decorated
  exhibited
  Stanley
  Stutz
  veil
68 old-fashioned
  mayor
69 Reed's
  ruts
70 . . .
71 rear
  hail

72 skim
  scenes
73 habit
  conversation
  United States
  prepared
74 . . .

**UNIT II**

75 . . .
76 Curtis
  Melvin
  wraps

492

  tucked
  cloakroom
  curious
77 navy
  invention
  inventor
78 recess
79 Paul
  Briggs
  fake
  serious
  expressions
80 disappoint
  demonstration*
  treatment
81 propeller
  metal
82 repeating
  magician
  Friday
  awful
83 pronounced
  grimly*
  abbreviation*
84 . . .
85 Thomas*
  Edison*

86 advance
  tawny*
  roaming
  noble*
  greets
  simple
  *Bengal*
  *discern*
  strolling
  view
  *lept*
  *leopard*
87 *caress*
  distinguish
  *prey*
  *novice*
  *nonplus*
  crocodiles
  thus
  weep
  chameleon*
  lizard

88 Crockett*
  Mississippi
  scout
  member
  Congress*

89 panther's*
  slept
90 . . .
91 appreciation*
92 enjoying
93 pickle
94 tinder*
  fading
  pucker
95 grizzly
  axis*
  stiffer
  cog*
96 steaks

97 griddle
  Bunyan*
  Dakotas
  hip
98 bunkhouses
  parachutes
  gongs
99 satisfied
  Ole
  grease
  sacks
  bacon
100 magnets
  lippity-cut
101 . . .
102 finally
  arranged
  position
  concrete
  sourdough*
103 according
  troop
104 chute
  pulleys*
  explode
  dynamite*
105 . . .

106 ancient*
  *Grecian*
  fiddle
  marmalade*
  tunes
  certainly
  *riddle*
  gaunt*
  *ravenous*
  gloomy
  intent
  *slay*
  *melody*
  beguiled*

107 *appeased*
  perplexes
  Hindu*

108 python*
  *advise*
  *measles*
  *inclined*
  improve
  merely
  *chastise*
  severely
  *Yucatan*

109 Alois*
  minister
  future*
  Basel*
  sale
  pale
110 August
  healthy
111 firm
112 scholar*
113 Sion
  president
  honest
114 expenses
  departed
115 wafer*
116 companions
  mistress
  miracle*
117 cured
  madam
  gaily
  chamois*
  peasants*
  amidst
118 . . .
119 intelligence*
  concerns
  robber
  midnight
  eleven
  sneak
120 bound
  congratula-
   tions
121 deeds

122 . . .
123 suggestion*
  puppets
124 . . .

493

494

495

365 craters*
366 Eopee*
    accomplished
367 gravity*
    relax
368 . . .
369 meekly
370 . . .

371 anti-gravity
    Dunn
    revenge
    Jupiter*
    adjutant
372 Arnold
    arithmetic
373 murmured
    professor
    Bullfinch
    scientist
    punishment
374 Euclid*
    laboratory
375 spare
    mimeograph
    satellites*
376 beaker
    insulating
    nervously
    society
    accidents
377 Willoughby
378 Grimes
379 soles
380 weird*
381 . . .

382 castaways*
    Glen
    Mars
    cadets*
    lurch*
383 vacuum*
384 Phobos*
    oxygen
    anticontact*
385 . . .
386 globe
387 capsules*
    electronic*
388 switched
    whether
    release
389 . . .
390 . . .
391 canals*
392 rapidly

393 arrangements
_____
394 bomber
    cruising*
    Rogers
395 cockpit
    plugged
    fuel
396 spite
    temperature
    degrees*
397 horizon*
    ounce
    Saberjet
398 various

399 missile*
    Cape Canav-
      eral*
    Florida
    Wernher*
    Von Braun*
400 launching
    information
    Grand Ba-
      hama*
    Puerto Rico*
401 military
    minus
402 four-stage
    solid
    chills
403 vents*
    moisture
404 cluster
405 arc*
406 pad
    delay
    Ernst*
    Stuhlinger*
407 . . .
408 proper
    New Jersey
    Washington
_____
409 universe

410 . . .
411 . . .
412 . . .
_____
**UNIT VIII**
413 . . .
414 Balto's*
    Nome

Alaska
diphtheria*
antitoxin*
territory
415 Tuesday
    Nenana*
416 huskies
417 Leonard*
    Seppala*
    zero
    Norton
    gee
    Togo
418 . . .
419 Olson
420 Gunnar*
    Kasson*
421 . . .
422 . . .
423 Solomon*
424 . . .
425 . . .
426 . . .
_____
427 *starveling*
    *naked*
    *soul*

428 Caribbean*
    breeches
    linen
429 spade
    pirate
430 yarn
    pistols
431 stranded
432 Wilkes
    mate
    navigating*
433 cask
434 Jamaica*
435 governor
    Spain
    traitor*
436 muttering
437 carpenter
438 . . .
439 . . .
440 . . .
441 . . .
442 bargain
443 . . .
_____
444 Donald*
    MacDer-
      mott*
    Vancouver*

Columbia*
fleet
445 protection
    Henri*
    LeGrand*
    portage*
446 sullen*
447 timber
    cautiously
    heaps
    Baptiste*
    Jacques*
448 . . .
449 rifle
450 *non*
451 . . .
452 style
453 plaid*
    clan*
    *oui*
454 . . .
455 *merci*
456 lobstick
457 childhood
458 Bairn*

459 cedar
    hasten
    *voyageurs*
    *undaunted**
    *dismay*

460 Hoosier*
    barbecue*
    Indiana
    bluff
    Wabash*
461 cranes
462 Ohio
463 . . .
464 hickory
    beef
    pork
    picnickers
465 . . .
466 . . .
467 . . .
468 . . .
469 marooned*
470 . . .
471 . . .
472 . . .
_____
473 . . .
474 column
    continent
    symbol
475 . . .